THE CAVE MAN'S HONEYMOON

WONDER BOOK
OF THE
WORLD'S PROGRESS

VOL. II
PREHISTORY • EARLY MAN

WONDER BOOK

OF THE

WORLD'S PROGRESS

By
HENRY SMITH WILLIAMS

IN TEN VOLUMES
Illustrated

•

VOLUME II
Prehistory
Early Man

FUNK & WAGNALLS COMPANY
NEW YORK AND LONDON

CONTENTS — VOL. II

PREHISTORY • EARLY MAN

INTRODUCTION

THIS volume deals chiefly with the development of animal life. Before turning to this story, however, it is desirable to give a brief outline of the history of the development of the land surfaces of the globe during the long period of time that elapsed between the appearance of the original continent in the southern hemisphere and the dominant activities of the highest type of animal life to which we now refer.

According to the theory which I put forward in *The Biography of Mother Earth*, to which reference has been made, the dominant factor in disturbing the equilibrium or balance of the earth, as a revolving body, was the development of life; and in particular the fact that both the vegetable and animal organisms, on dying, leave permanent remains in the form of silicates or carbonates of lime—the matter of shell and bones—which becomes a part of the mineral mass of the earth's surface and ultimately builds up the strata of stony matter. The aggregate of rocky strata built up in the ocean depths of the world by animal deposit, and by detritus passed on from preexisting land surfaces, is something like 100 miles in depth; not in any one place, but in the aggregate, as measured in different regions of the globe. As the matter built up is constantly being worn down when the continent is elevated above the ocean surface, it is impossible to judge of the original depth of strata in any given place.

Obviously the enormous weight of thousands of feet of stone disturbs very materially the balance of the earth's crust. Our earth is a whirling globe, and such a globe tends to take a spheroidal form. Everyone knows that the earth is such a spheroidal or roundish body, flattened at the poles, and correspondingly bulging at the equator. Such a form is called the ideal spheroid of rotation.

If the surface of the earth were of homogeneous material, and did not change, our globe would then assume a spheroidal shape and would so remain as long as it continued to rotate at a uniform speed. But the organic changes, and the changes due to the action of the elements, appreciably modify the form of the surface, so that there is a constant tendency to shift material from one part of the earth's surface to another, to maintain or reestablish balance. The actual surface of the earth is called the geoid. Obviously this differs quite materially from the ideal spheroid. In the theory of continental shifting as developed in *The Biography of Mother Earth,* this discrepancy between the ideal spheroid and the actual geoid is spoken of as geoid-spheroid balance. The theory which attempts to account for the changes has been given the name of geoid-balance hypothesis.

I shall not here elaborate this theory, beyond pointing out that it is the whirling motion of the earth that is the determining force believed to be operative. The same force that originally molded the form of the earth into an oblate spheroid continues to act in the attempt to restore this spheroidal form, when it has been modified through the building up and the wearing down of land masses.

It is held that the original southern continent became unwieldy, ultimately overbalancing the earth, and so disturbing the ideal spheroidal form that there was in effect an urge operating to push the Antarctic Continent equatorward. The force ultimately availed to split it apart, until one fragment after another was thrust toward the equator—leaving, however, a residual part that is the Antarctic Continent of today. This continent, however, is not in its original location. Perhaps portions now directly at the pole were then far removed, so as to lie within the temperate or even the subtropical zone. That is why evidences of coal formation have been found near the pole—as reported provisionally by earlier explorers and confirmed by Admiral Byrd.

It was perhaps during the time of the great Ice Age in the northern hemisphere that the present Antarctic Continent was thrust back toward the south pole, to restore balance.

Other fragments of the original Antarctic Continent, subsequently separated and slowly propelled northward, represent the continental masses of today—Africa, South America, and Australia. Another continental mass, called Lemuria, drifted into collision with Asia, and is represented by the southern portion of that continent, including India.

We shall have occasion to speak of the original continent in the southern hemisphere as Gondwanaland. The main continental mass that first broke away and floated northward—comprising what ultimately became the continents of Eurasia and North America—will be spoken of as Holarctica.

I shall not here go into details of the breaking up of this original Antarctic Continent, a full account of which is given in the book just referred to. For the present purpose, it is better to disregard these highly controversial aspects of the subject, confining attention to the development of the animal population, regarding the general trend of which there is no difference of opinion among paleontologists.

A word should be said about the time element. In *The Biography of Mother Earth* I adopt a time schedule which allots something over three billion years as the age of the earth's crust since it became possibly habitable to living organisms, but I have no quarrel with anyone who wishes to fix a two-billion-year period instead. The only thing to be insisted on is that the period during which life has been evolving on the globe is vastly longer than the geologists of the elder days supposed. But no one can gain a very clear notion as to the meaning of the word million, let alone billion. Let it suffice that time is very long, and the evolutionary progress a very slow one. Dated chronologies are merely a matter of convenience. If they have served any other purpose it is perhaps to bring home to us the truth that the human race has been a very long time in reaching its present status, and that its future development must necessarily be slow—a fact which would-be reformers often find it hard to understand.

Let us, then, go back in imagination a matter of three billion years or so, and take up the story of the development of prehistoric life.

CHRONOLOGICAL SUMMARY OF GEOLOGIC HISTORY

Total Time Schedule, 3,200,000,000 years.

Archeozoic Era	900,000,000 years
Proterozoic Era	600,000,000 years
Paleozoic Era	900,000,000 years
Mesozoic Era	450,000,000 years
Cenozoic Era	350,000,000 years

THE PALEOZOIC ERA

A stretch of 900,000,000 years, divided into six major Periods, during which there is progress of the most spectacular character.

Pre-View of the Paleozoic Era, by Periods:

Cambrian Period	100,000,000 years	}	
Ordovician "	250,000,000 "	} Age of Invertebrates	
Silurian "	100,000,000 "	}	
Devonian "	100,000,000 "	Age of Fishes	
Carboniferous "	250,000,000 "	Age of Coal	
Permian "	75,000,000 "	Age of Amphibians	

SEA ANEMONES AND CORALS

I

WE VISIT HOLARCTICA IN THE CAMBRIAN PERIOD

IMAGINE a vast stretch of territory which—as one might view it from an airplane—is relatively flat, tho of varied elevation above sea-level. It is everywhere absolutely arid as regards land surface. There is no slightest semblance of vegetable or animal life, past or present. The general surface is covered with rocks that are more or less eroded and weather-beaten. The sides of the rather low mountains are gullied by water and chiseled by wind-borne sand. There are great areas covered with volcanic ash and tufa. Other areas of desert sands, wind-rippled in characteristic fashion. In certain regions there are boulders and clay-beds that suggest glacial action. Elsewhere there are masses of rock blasted from mountainsides by the elements, and rounded into boulder-like form by the action of sun and wind and water. There are gravel-beds, too, and exposed layers of stratified rocks that suggest an under-water origin. It is obvious that parts of the land have been elevated out of the sea. But nowhere is there the slightest modicum of the dark, conglomerate surface-substance which one could term "soil" in the ordinary acceptance of the word.

Yet there is no dearth of water. There are rivers rushing toward the northern seashore, with minor tributaries gulleying the mountains and plateaus. There are vast inland lakes and lagoons. Toward the center of the continent there are great invading seas, hundreds of miles in extent, connecting with the ocean at the southern border of the far-flung land-mass.

But the river-banks, the lake-shores, the borders of the seas are alike untenanted by any wisp of vegetation. They are as barren, as arid, as forlorn as the most ghastly stretch of sand or volcanic ash. From border to border of the vast continent—throughout the whole of its millions of square miles of territory — there is not to be found one blade of grass. Nor the slightest trace of a creeping or crawling thing. Not even a burrowing worm. Not so much as a fleck of fungus on a rock surface or a strand of moss in a crevice. It is a continent absolutely untenanted. Not a realm of death, but a land surface that has never known life, even in its most primordial form.

But if we turn from this arid land surface to the waters, the scene instantly changes. We shall find the ocean, the lagoons, the lakes, the estuaries, the inland seas, teeming with living creatures of a thousand forms. Paradoxical tho it may seem, the waters everywhere swarm with living populations, while the land is absolutely tenantless. But the paradox vanishes when we come to understand that the members of this prolific flora and fauna are all of relatively primitive types. They are confined to the waters because no one of them has yet learned the secret of breathing in air, and the other secrets of land-habitation. After all these millennia, no air-breathing plant or animal has been evolved. Nor has any plant yet developed tissues that would give it stability without the support of water-pressure. And tho the animals are of varied forms, and many have the protection of shells, there is no creature here, nor has there ever been one in the world, that has even a suggestion of the interior skeleton the basis of which is a backbone.

There is nothing remotely resembling a fish—let alone an amphibian or a reptile—in this entire conglomerate population.

The creatures that are here, however, are of diversified and interesting forms. The ameboid flecks of protoplasm—one-celled organisms—that were the lords of creation of the elder day have left descendants more or less like themselves, to be sure. But they have left other descendants, now ever increasing in number, that have learned tricks of living undreamed of in the good old days. These have aggregated into colonies, and developed systems of cooperation through which the business of living is carried forward with enhanced efficiency. Some groups of cells have specialized in locomotion. Others in the digestion of food. Yet others in the collecting and piling together of molecules of silica or of limestone to form protective coverings for the entire community.

There is such harmony of action in a community like this that one thinks of it, not as a group, but as a single individual. In particular when the community as a whole, thanks to its motor department, has the power of moving about through the water. Here, for instance, is a long-drawn-out community that wriggles along through the mud, which, for want of a better name, we may term a worm. And there is a vast stationary community, obviously made up of living units, which we call a sponge. Other not unfamiliar forms we may name jelly-fishes—tho the second word is highly anticipatory, since there is no such thing as a fish in all the world at this time. Nor will be for millions of years to come.

There are shelled communities galore — clam-like brachiopods and snail-like gastropods. The communities (or individuals) of a given region number thousands or millions, closely resembling one another. In a neighboring region there are other groups so different that — despite a family resemblance—we account them as of different "species," and, had we time for it, would give them different names. Yet all are descendants of a single primordial brachiopod-colony (or individual). The present diversity has resulted from response to altered conditions of the environment as one younger generation after another has been forced to emigrate along the shores or through the shallower sea-beds. Such emigration was the only alternative to starving through over-populating of the mother-territory.

Tho we shall find these varied creatures—say the clam-like brachiopods—all along the shores and through the interior seas of the entire continent (the total stretch of which, it will be recalled, is something like ten thousand by three thousand miles), we must understand that all have come, directly or indirectly, from the same original locus. Their rate of migration has been inconceivably slow. To gain anything like a clear conception of its slowness, and of the gradualness of the changes that have in the end wrought the transformations of size and shape and appearance that we observe, we must attune our minds to a totally unaccustomed time-scale. We must endeavor to conceive that a "century"—the span of the longest human life—is an invisibly minute *point* of time. A thousand years is scarcely less negligible. At most, centuries and millennia in the geologic scale rank as seconds and minutes of human history.

We must understand, then, that if our exploration of Holarctica were to continue for a mere ten thousand years, or even a hundred thousand, we should think ourselves in a changeless world. Our diaries at the end of the century of centuries would contain much the same record as at its beginning. No marked change of topography, beyond a few volcanic outbursts and earthquake faultings; or the slight shift of a river-course, the widening of a bay through the action of waves, or the filling in of an estuary—all of negligible importance. The animal population of the waters has been equally static. Every creature has seemed to produce offspring precisely like itself—or with only such trifling discrepancies of detail as always exist between parent and progeny. This colony of brachiopods, say, has spread a few miles into an estuary not previously inhabited. That colony has died out in a lagoon at the other side of the estuary. But in general, speaking broadly, nothing of consequence seems to have happened in the organic world in the hundred thousand years of our observation.

Yet the truth is that there has been perpetual change. Only our senses are too blunt to observe it or to appreciate its import. Could we but know it, the continent as a whole has slid forward a little (steadily or with spasmodic earthquake thrusts at intervals) under stress of the perpetual thrust of inertia, striving as always for geoid balance. The northern border is perhaps a third of a mile nearer the equator than it was a hundred thousand years ago. The contour of that border has also changed. In places it is elevated by a good many feet; in other places depressed. There have been oscillations of large interior areas, had we instruments delicate enough to note them. Inevitable oscillations, when you reflect that the entire continent is, after all, only a thin raft of sial floating in a semifluid sea of magma.

It is these oscillations, in part, that have caused the estuaries to widen here and narrow there, as their shores shifted their level. But deposits of detritus from the rivers have added to the effect, by sheer weight causing settling. This effect has been accentuated by the perpetual accumulation of the silicious coverings of myriads of diatoms, the calcareous secretions of other algæ, and the shells and chitinous members of hordes of brachiopods, trilobites, and other members of the living population. Beds of this detritus have accumulated, to form future strata of shale and limestone many feet in thickness, even during the relatively brief period of our sojourn.

As to the vegetable and animal populations themselves, there has been not stasis—as our cursory examination seemed to show—but perennial change. Perhaps this does not apply to certain of the most primitive types of single-celled creatures, which reproduce themselves by fission, and which, finding pelagic conditions almost changeless, themselves appear to remain unmodified. But these are now but a remnant, of relative unimportance, in a world which they once dominated. For the rest—the vast multitudes of multicellular organisms —we shall be near the truth if we say that no two individuals are ever precisely alike; that each parent differs from the other, and that every offspring differs somewhat from either parent. "Like produces like" is a formula of only the most general import. Like never really does produce like, nor ever can, since reproduction implies the union of diverse elements. The phrase is self-nugatory.

In every member of each new generation, then, there are the potentialities of progressive—or of decadent— racial change. Where environmental conditions are relatively stationary, however, there will be a host of influences favoring the individual that departs least from the average ancestral traits that have been developed

through endless generations of response to that environment. Individuals that depart widely from the average
will, by that token, be less well adapted to secure food
and to escape the enemies of their race. So they will
have fewer progeny, on the average, than more typical
individuals. Otherwise stated, in the struggle for existence, the fittest individuals will survive, and tend to perpetuate their fitness through heredity. And "fitness,"
for any given species at a given time, implies the pos-
session of certain "average" traits that are typical of
that species.

And so, in an unchanging environment, a species may
remain apparently stationary generation after generation, and millennium after millennium. Hence it is not
strange that we should find the population of the waters
of Holarctica seemingly unchanged in the period of our
observation.

But let us extend the term of our sojourn. We are
independent of time, and have agreed to think in terms
of millions of years. Suppose we take another Rip Van
Winkle sleep, compassing this time not a mere hundred
thousand years, but a hundred times that. While these
ten million years elapse, changes go on no more rapidly
than before. But now the cumulative effects have become sufficiently obvious to attract our attention. The
changes, to be sure, are not enormous—for ten million
years is not a long stretch in the history of a planet—
but they are not altogether negligible.

For simplicity's sake suppose we confine attention to
a simple race of organisms, selecting the one that lies
nearly at the top of the organic scale, so far as yet
evolved. Here in abundance is a member of the sub-
kingdom of Arthropods, or jointed creatures (lobsters,
spiders, insects of a later period), which is called a Trilo-

SEA ANEMONES AND CORALS

bite, because of the conspicuous three lobes of its shelled body. It is a creature not destined to survive till the Age of Man. But its fitness for the conditions of life in the waters of Holarctica in the Cambrian and subsequent periods is attested by its abundance. The family proliferated into thousands of species, before vertebrates came to make its life unduly hazardous.

There is one tribe of this race of Trilobites, for which classifiers devised the generic name *Olenellus*, which merits our special attention. It wears a frontal helmet-shell somewhat like that of a horseshoe crab; a mid-region armor of jointed pieces, and a long spiny tail. The tail in particular one must notice, because it seems rather needlessly long and of doubtful utility. Yet it perhaps seems a trifle shorter and less conspicuous than the tails of the ancestral Trilobites—in the main, similar to the present one, which we examined in these waters a short time since—that is to say, ten million years ago.

One cannot be sure that the tail really has changed. Surely it cannot have changed much in a mere ten million years, during which the continent has shifted position by only about thirty miles, and the character of the watery environment seems scarcely to have changed at all.

But let us exercise our prerogative, and retire again to slumberland, this time not for ten million years only, but for five or six times that period. Now there has been time for the cumulative effect of a series of infinitesimal changes. It is like skipping a strip of cinema-film, on which successive pictures seem identical, to find that the scene has now totally changed. Dragging our dredge along the sea-bottom, we scoop up any number of Trilobites, but we find among them no single specimen of the spine-tailed *Olenellus* we are seeking. Apparently our ancient surmise was right. That tail was an encumbrance. At any rate, it came to be an encumbrance when conditions changed in the Cambrian sea. And so, in the long stretch of generations, as from time to time a Trilobite was born with a tendency to a shorter tail, that individual was favored in the struggle for existence and tended to found a family of short-tailed Trilobites. That was the beginning of the end of the tail-end of *Olenellus.*

And then, after the lapse of about fifty million years, longtailed Trilobites having been weeded out generation after generation by the struggle for existence, and shorter and shorter tails coming into fashion, tails were altogether tabu. The transformation was so notable that geologists of the future would think it appropriate to let the disappearance of spine-tailed *Olenellus* mark the end of a geological sub-period, referred to as the Lower Cambrian.

To complete the story, it should be added that the tribe of Trilobites that supplanted *Olenellus* (dubbed *Paradoxides*) was similarly dominant for another term of fifty million years or so, typifying the Middle Cambrian sub-period. Its successor, called *Dikellocephalus,* in turn dominated the Upper Cambrian, and by the fossil-hunters was to be regarded as so important that they rang down the curtain on the Cambrian Period when this round-tailed descendant of the ancient spine-tailed Trilobite ceased to exist.

Not that the Trilobites had any such importance as this might seem to imply, in the actual history of Mother Earth. Not that there was even any world-wide catastrophe to mark the time when the third type of Trilobite disappeared (leaving, however, abundant successors of modified types). Merely that it is convenient for students of the history of our planet to have guide-marks, even as in human history; and that the three types of Trilobites that successively populated the waters of Holarctica (and spread elsewhere across shallow intervening seas), serve as mementoes of chronological sequence, and indices to epochs.

We must guard against the inference, however, that the strata in which a certain type of Trilobite — say *Olenellus*—is preserved as a fossil, if found in different regions of the globe, are necessarily contemporaneous. Under ordinary conditions, the wide geographical distribution of a race of animals or plants is a very slow process. Before a species reaches the confines of a new habitat, it may have become extinct in the old habitat. It may continue to thrive in the new habitat (changed specifically no doubt, but generically still recognizable) for tens of thousands of years. Thus the Trilobites that mark the "Cambrian" of Australia, Tasmania, or India may have lived millions of years later than those that similarly mark the "Cambrian" of Holarctica, as revealed in the strata of present China, United States, and England.

As a modern example of the same type of discrepancy, note that some future geologist might suppose elephant remains deposited this year in some morass of central Africa to be exactly contemporaneous with elephant remains from Siberia, Alaska, or southern California. Or he might suppose the Australia of the twentieth century to be coeval with the Europe of perhaps two hundred million years ago, because of the discovery of fossil remains of the early type of mammals known as Marsupials in what would be assumed to be corresponding strata of both continents.

SUBMARINE LIFE, AGE OF INVERTEBRATES

II

THE SECOND-BILLIONTH BIRTHDAY

MOTHER EARTH was now passing through the concluding hundred million or two hundred million years of her second billion—as nearly as her age can be reckoned. It proved to be a highly interesting and significant period of her mid-life development. One milestone was the first appearance of land in the northern hemisphere, as the prow of the Holarctic continent slowly nosed its way across the equator. Another, and even more notable, marked the first appearance of plants on the land surface of the same continent. As yet there were no air-breathing animals, but these would presently find their way to the land, in the wake of the plants, upon which all animal life is dependent for existence.

But the most notable incident of all—in some ways the most momentous, in human estimate, of any event since the first appearance of life itself—was the development in some favored lagoon of a strange creature that had so varied from the ancestral type that it could scarcely be classed as Trilobite or Eucrustacean or Eurypterid or any allied jointed creature. Even less as gastropod or cephalopod or other member of the molluscan division. It was a creature so different that the classifiers of a later day, coming upon its fossil remains, would declare it the type of a new sub-kingdom, and name it Ostracoderm—the shell-skinned animal. In the cartilage that ran as a supporting rod throughout the length of the creature's body, the classifiers would see the adumbration of a backbone. They would hail the tiny, fish-like Ostracoderm as the forerunner of the great sub-kingdom of Vertebrates.

In the contemporary world, we may well believe, the strange new creature created no sensation whatsoever. If considered at all by huge Trilobite and lordly Cephalopod, it must have been thought a regrettable monstrosity, of dubious digestibility, owing to that bizarre head-shield of shell. The scales on the tailward part of its body did not add to its attractiveness, from a gastronomic viewpoint — which of course was the salient viewpoint of the period.

There were, to be sure, numberless other creatures in the water population of the time that had similar disabilities. Indeed, no creature that lacked some manner of protective covering was likely to have a long racial history, in that swarming world of predators. But the Ostracoderm decidedly starred in bizarre ugliness of feature and contour. A squeamish member of the genus *Homo,* viewing the remains of this remote forebear, might be disposed to renounce interest in genealogy. Yet even by such renunciation he could not perhaps altogether escape the humiliating recollection that the very earliest of his vertebrate ancestors had been revealed as a character so obviously plebeian.

Nevertheless, the potentialities of great things — as mankind estimates greatness—were in the cartilaginous near-backbone of this ugly duckling, or in the spermatic *genes* that would cause this useful new structure to be transmitted, with betterments, to a long line of posterity. Comparatively few scores of millions of years would now elapse before the descendants of the despised Ostracoderm would be the acknowledged lords of creation; a position not to be achieved, however, without desperate struggles in the face of odds that must often have seemed quite hopeless.

It would be pleasant to record that the advent of the creature of such potentialities coincided with Mother Earth's two-billionth birthday. But data are lacking that would justify such an assertion as an historical fact. Yet it may well enough have been so, despite the lack of evidence. At least there is no evidence to the contrary, and the fossil records reveal the earliest Ostracoderm in strata of the period called Ordovician, following the Cambrian and preceding the Silurian. During this period, according to the chronology adopted by the present biographer, the two-billionth birthday must have occurred.

Unfortunately for the stickler for precise chronological synchronism, the Ordovician period must be admitted to have covered something like two hundred and fifty million years. This gives a good deal of latitude for error of adjustment between anniversary and natal day, respectively, of Mother Earth and her new inhabitant. After all, however, the thing of importance is the appearance of the new visitor, rather than the precise time of his coming. Suffice it that somewhere about the close of the second billion-year period of geologic history, the ancestor of all vertebrates was born into a waiting world. And somehow escaped destruction.

Let us follow the fortunes of the descendants of the little Ordovician monstrosity. We shall learn that their story equals in importance, and far surpasses in interest, the story of continental origins and migrations; of the building and wearing down of mountains; and of all other phenomena that enter into the physical history of the earth's changing face.

THE AGE OF FISHES

III

THE AGE OF FISHES

BY far the greater part of the vast continent of Holarctica now lay within the tropic zone. Its northern border was halfway to the Tropic of Cancer (tho not following accurately the parallel, being somewhat obliquely tilted, with the eastern end farthest advanced). The triangular southern extremity projected somewhat below the Tropic of Capricorn. Owing to the form of the continent as a whole, the larger moiety of its surface lay directly in the equatorial belt.

Throughout a territory of such geographical location, the climatic conditions would be relatively uniform. Nor would they greatly differ, as regards average temperature in particular, from the shore regions of the northern borders of the other continents, Gondwanaland and Lemuria, both of which lay near the tropic belt. As Holarctica, its bulk now north of the equator, assumed a northeasterly trend, its southeastern border (future Europe) cannot have been widely separated from the northwestern border of Gondwanaland (future South America). The intervening stretch of sea was doubtless shallow. The greater depth of ocean still lay farther to the north. Thus there was opportunity for communication between the pelagic populations.

The "Age of Fishes," to which we have come, is technically known as the Devonian period. As a whole, it compasses a stretch of about one hundred million years. It is therefore a significant, but not an unduly pro-

31

tracted, interval in the history of our continent. Its signal claim to attention is that it was the time when vertebrate creatures first assumed importance, and gave sure augury of their great destiny. These vertebrates were fishes. Their primitive ancestors, descended in turn from the Ostracoderm of our Ordovician acquaintance, had indeed been abroad in the preceding (Silurian) period, but had not then sufficiently advanced to give clear assurance that they were the forerunners of a tribe that would successfully challenge the supremacy of Mollusk and Arthropod. Now, however, in the Devonian time, it was obvious that these new vertebrate creatures represented a decidedly successful experiment in animal architecture. They could be counted on to go far.

A prime characteristic of the vertebrate structure is that, in addition to the spine which encompasses a nerve-apparatus called the spinal cord, there is an anterior bony development in which there is lodged a larger grouping of nerve cells to form a brain. This is a great storehouse of sense-impressions, and a kind of telephone "central" that makes possible the interchange and comparison of perceptions. Otherwise stated, this new organ, the brain, is the organ of Mind.

Doubtless our primeval vertebrate ancestors of the Age of Fishes were notable for development of brawn rather than for the more esthetic and appealing properties of brain-action. But on the other hand, they undoubtedly could have made a good showing in any mentality-test applied to themselves in comparison with their neighbors in general. Indeed, their "intelligence quotient" would doubtless have set a standard hardly attainable by any mollusk or arthropod of them all.

And as to the matter of teeth, and how to use them, there was no non-vertebrate that could give the better-equipped fishes even a pretense of adequate competition.

This was not true at the outset, however. The earliest vertebrates were by no means heroic figures. Evolution does not work like that. A new race that is to become dominant does not suddenly appear at the peak of its power, sprung from the loins of a race hitherto dominant. Far from it. The forerunner of the new race appears as an insignificant weakling, sprung from obscure parents, and itself, as an individual, destined to live no less obscurely. Indeed, it is only by straining the meaning of words that we can speak of any individual whatsoever as the first member of a new race. There is no first member. There is no sharp dividing line between the old order and the new. There is an unending series of generations, each but infinitesimally different from the one before. The most that can be said is that a genetic line of organisms is trending in a slightly modified direction. Certain old characteristics are being emphasized, certain others minimized. A few more nerve cells are being aggregated in the head. Certain epidermal scales about the mouth are tending to harden and assume a cutting edge. Then, after thousands of generations of such modification, it appears that the aggregation of nerve cells is really notable, and we call it a brain. It appears also that the modified scales are so hardened and sharpened and adjusted that they better and better serve the purpose of clutching food, and we call them teeth.

And since, for purposes of description and classification at any rate, things must have a beginning, we say that this individual is the first fish. If we are candid, we may add that, had we first met him in the flesh, before he had justified himself through his descendants, we should not have been likely to predict for him a brilliant future. Which only goes to suggest the familiar truth that looks are deceptive.

Even as to looks, however, perhaps the earliest fishes do not make too bad a showing, in comparison with their contemporaries—the only fair test. At any rate they are built on a very practical and seaworthy model. A model, indeed, that has been followed, without major modification, by every successful speed-craft, animate or inanimate, of air or water—bird, seal, or porpoise; boat, motorcar, or aircraft—from that remote day to this.

It is no small thing to set such a precedent as that. The primitive fish was an insignificant creature, if you will, but its trim figure and its alert brain were the harbingers of sure success. It could escape enemies that mollusk and crustacean could not elude. It could secure prey that would escape a less alert hunter. It would win, beyond peradventure, in the all but heart-breaking struggle for existence.

And win it surely did. A scant hundred million years elapsed from the day of the first selachians (primitive fish), back there in the Silurian, to the Devonian mid-period in which the waters swarmed not alone with selachians grown to shark-like proportions, but with even more formidable Arthrodirans in bony armor, and Ganoids that have modern representatives in gar-pike and sturgeon. Bony fishes of the type of salmon and cod had not yet appeared. But a strange creature called a lungfish developed the amazing capacity to breathe in air no less than in water. The time was at hand when animal life would invade the land, where certain plants had recently gained a footing.

Plants, no longer of the most primitive types, were spreading across the continent, drawing carbon from the air, and other nourishment from the crumbled rock that was nascent soil. Vertebrate creatures (even if only fishes) dominated the waters, and were preparing to invade the land. A new world, indeed, is this period called Devonian. Great days are ahead, and the tide of progress will now move faster. And at every stage the history of Mother Earth will be documented with fossil records in gratifying profusion.

CARBONIFEROUS AGE

IV

WHEN THE COAL BEDS WERE A-MAKING

WHO could believe that Holarctica, as we now visit it, is the same land which we recall as a barren waste at the beginning of the Era, scarcely six hundred million years ago? With bewildering suddenness, in the course of the recent period of a hundred or two hundred million years since the plants escaped from the waters and learned the trick of air-breathing, the forms of vegetable life have become diversified and elaborated. Since they learned how to make woody stems, by deposit of carbonaceous and silicious material, they can raise their heads into the air, thrust their roots into the forming soil for support, and continue to grow almost interminably. Multitudes of them are upward of a hundred feet in height, and with trunks four and five feet in diameter.

In the moist air rich in carbon dioxid, and under stimulus of the tropic sun, these plants, individually enormous, grow in jungle-like profusion. Despite their size and general appearance, they are not trees in the modern sense, but exaggerated ferns and club mosses and "horse-tails." The jungle is a Brobdingnagian fernery, such as no soil but the richest, and no climate other than tropical or at least subtropical, could maintain. Only while Holarctica is drifting through tropic zones can this ultra-luxuriant vegetation persist. Nor, of course, can it flourish in Gondwanaland, or in Lemuria except as these continents are similarly, in their turn, drifting into the equatorial belt.

For the moment, however, conditions are ideal for the flourishing of these exuberant jungles in Holarctica, especially across its central latitudes, where fresh-water lagoons occupy vast stretches of territory. Here in an Amazonian belt of perpetual summer, the huge tree-ferns and tree-mosses, together with hosts of lesser confrères, perennially compass the cycle of growth and decay. Their remains accumulate and undergo compression as the swampy surface settles. They form layers of peat that will in time turn to lignite, and in places to the compact mineral to be known in the remote future as coal.

The lagoons where conditions are ideal for this process of coal-formation occupy, to be sure, only minor areas of the surface of the vast continent—tho individual stretches of jungle may be hundreds of miles in extent. Moreover, local conditions naturally change, in the course of time, as the continental surface oscillates, and as the slow northward—or northeastward—drift continues. We must not fail to note that this "Carboniferous Period," or Age of the Coal Measures, covers a stretch of about 275 million years, during which the Holarctic Continent as a whole shifts its position by perhaps a thousand miles.

Only by bearing this in mind shall we understand the formation of coal beds which in the broad view may be said to be of "contemporary" or "simultaneous" origin at the northern border of the Holarctic Continent (present Spitzbergen, Siberia, Alaska, Greenland) and at the central portion now represented by the Pennsylvania region and the coal measures of Great Britain, Germany, and Russia—not to mention similar deposits found in northern Africa, India, and Australia. "Contemporary," as we use the word in reviewing the life-history of Mother Earth, must often be interpreted as meaning "somewhere within the same quarter-billion or half-billion term of years."

The essential thing, however, in our present estimate, is that in tracing the itinerary of the Holarctic Continent, we find it crossing the tropic zone at precisely the period when, according to the geological records as interpreted from a quite different standpoint, the coal-beds were forming. The continent drifted on across the zones, entering latitudes where coal-forming jungles could no longer flourish, and carrying the tropic-formed coal-beds ultimately into Arctic regions where by no conceivability could they have originated—and where, by their presence, they caused profound mystification among several generations of latter-day geologists.

But to us, who have witnessed in imagination the formation of the coal-beds there in tropical Holarctica, and who are to follow the northward itinerary of the continent to its termination, there is nothing mysterious about, say, the coal-mines of Spitzbergen. The only thing inexplicable is that "reasoning" mortals should suppose that these relics of tropical jungles—these products of sunlight—could have originated in regions where half the year is night, and the other moiety only a slightly accentuated twilight.

But let that pass. Our concern is with the course of events in Holarctica of the Carboniferous period, not with twentieth-century interpretations.

As we proceed, we must readjust our view—rather paradoxically—about the importance of the coal-forming jungles that so vividly impressed us. After all, these forests of tree-ferns and their allies occupy only a minor part of the vast territory. The coal-beds they are forming, however important for future human affairs, will constitute only a scant two per cent of the total rock-strata being prepared by sedimentation and by the activities of myriads of lowly creatures of the waters. The elements are wearing away every land surface as of old. The products of erosion are being silted into sea-bed and lagoon. And new legions of foraminifers and radiolarians and sponges and corals and brachiopods and their ilk are contributing their silicious or calcareous coverings to the general fund of rock-making material.

Prominent among these lowly continent-builders—and so abundant that their remains are making what will ultimately represent thousands of feet of limestone beds—are certain creatures called crinoids, or "sea lilies." These are not plants, as their nickname might seem to imply, but animals of the sub-kingdom of Echinoderms. But in their mature state they are flower-like in general appearance, having a long, jointed, calcareous stem that is attached to the sea-bottom, and a tentacled body that resembles—at least vaguely—some types of chrysanthemums. Few other denizens of the sea are more decorative, and few are more active in extracting calcium from the water, and adding it to the substance of the continent on the borders of which they live.

So abundant are these limestone-makers that they become a significant factor in adding to the mass of the continent. Thus they do their bit toward further disturbing the geoid-spheroid balance, and thereby hastening (even if only in infinitesimal measure) the speed of northward migration of Holarctica. By the same token they are bringing nearer the time of extinction of their own race. They will not find the colder northern waters a fitting or congenial habitat.

These crinoids, however, albeit interesting, are creatures of no vast significance in the organic scale. There are multitudes of creatures of varied types in the sea that would equally repay particular observation, had we time for it. There are still great cephalopods, and eight-foot eurypterids; and the fishes have increased in numbers and advanced in all-round development. But chief interest, for any one with an eye to the future, lies in the creatures that, following the example of the plants, have made their way out of the water, and learned to breathe oxygen from the air.

Notable among these were myriapods, spiders, and scorpions—which had, indeed, made their appearance as early as the Devonian period. Also early representatives of the tribe of Insects, which was destined to have most significant influence in the struggle for existence of plant and animal life throughout the future.

Even more directly significant, in the human view, was the appearance of a modified descendant of a cousin of the lung-fish of the Devonian (dubbed "wingfish"), which had so increased its efficiency as an air-breather that in its mature form it depended altogether on this method of securing oxygen, even tho still spending much of its time under water. This anomalous creature came to be known as an Amphibian. Among its modern descendants, the one that has perhaps held closest to the ancestral type is the familiar frog. Among those that have departed more widely from the ancestral type, yet which retain many salient features of the original, is Man himself.

This amphibian, earliest of vertebrates adequately equipped for air-breathing, was a creature of most extraordinary architectural design. Between it and its ancestral prototype, the lung-fish, there were of course millions of generations. Multitudes of experiments had been made in the modification of the basic vertebral column and brain-case, and in bony appendages that had developed into fins in the fish, and were now being adapted to locomotion along a land surface. No doubt there were almost endless failures—modified structures that did not prove to be advantageous, and led to the elimination of their unfortunate possessors. But here and there a change proved useful, and better enabled its possessor to secure food or to escape its enemies—these being the crucial tests.

And at last the time had come, here in the Carboniferous period—the time when the coal-beds were forming—when the modified descendant of the wing-fish was a creature quite marvelously equipped for competition in the battle of life. Its spinal column and skull were relatively far advanced. Its muscular apparatus and its four legs, with their three main segments, were so near perfection that they were to serve as models for all classes of vertebrate creatures throughout the future. And the same astounding truth holds for the main organs of the interior mechanism, except that the heart was ultimately to be so improved as to give to each of the two kinds of blood an independent channel of circulation.

That such a degree of near-perfection—such unqualified perfection of architectural plan—should have been attained by a creature which, in the estimate of its later descendants, ranks near the foot of the vertebrate scale, is almost unbelievable. But we must realize that the Amphibian (or Batrachian), appearing toward the close of the Devonian, had back of it a line of ancestry covering a longer period than all geologic time subsequent to the Devonian. The really great hurdles in the progress of organic life had been triumphantly taken before the Amphibian arrived. The origin of living matter itself. The aggregation of cells into unified communities. The development of specialized organs. The evolvement of a higher nervous system, and the inclosure of its central parts in a bony covering. All these were matters of history. After the Amphibian, there was no really fundamental change, in comparable sense, to be made. In the broad view, all vertebrate creatures from Amphibian to Man are beings of the same *genre*—just as, technically, they rank as members of the same sub-kingdom.

DINOSAUR EGGS

AGE OF REPTILES, EARLY PERIOD

THE MESOZOIC ERA

This Era, known as the "Age of Reptiles," covers 450,000,000 years — *Anno Vitæ* 2,400,000,001 to 2,850,000,000. It is divided into three major periods, as follows:

Triassic Period	. . . .	100,000,000 years
Jurassic "	. . . .	100,000,000 "
Cretaceous "	. . . .	250,000,000 "

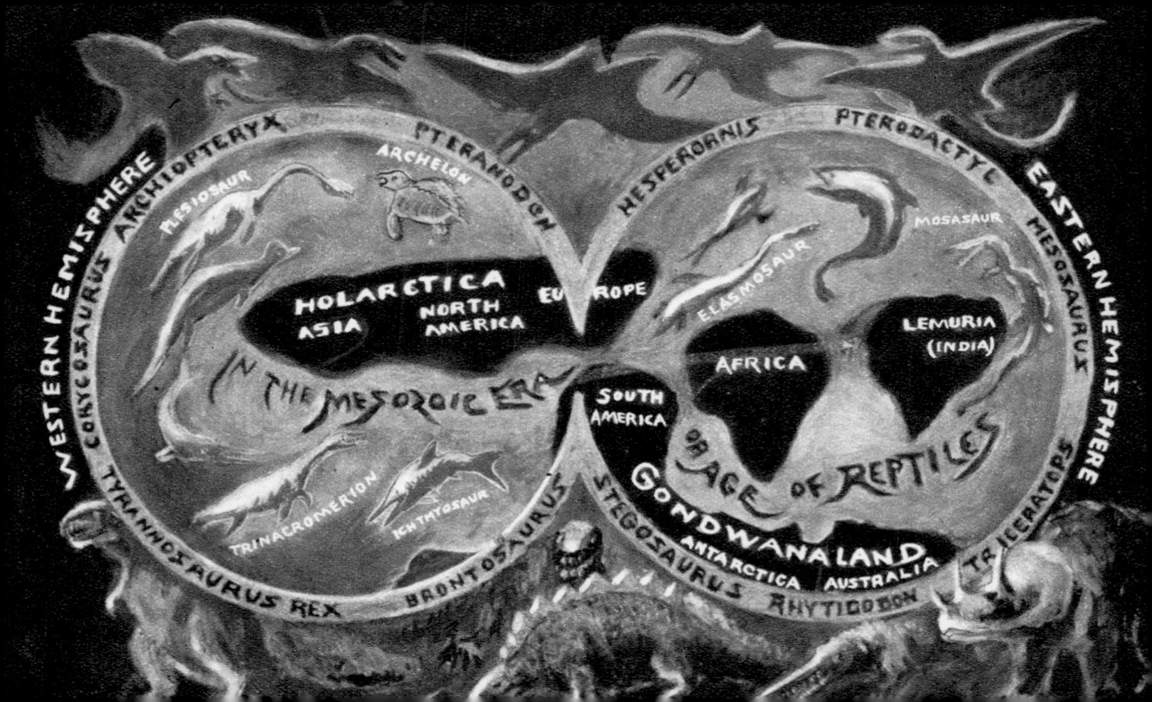

EASTERN HEMISPHERE

MESOSAURUS

MOSASAUR

PTERODACTYL

LEMURIA (INDIA)

TRICERATOPS

PLESIOSAUR

AFRICA

HESPERORNIS

OR "AGE OF REPTILES"

GONDWANALAND

ANTARCTICA

AUSTRALIA

RHYTIDODON

STEGOSAURUS

SOUTH AMERICA

EUROPE

PTERANODON

ARCHELON

HOLARCTICA
NORTH AMERICA

ASIA

IN THE MESOZOIC ERA

RHYTIDODON

TRINACROMERUM

BRONTOSAURUS

RESTOSAUR

ARCHIOPTERYX

WESTERN HEMISPHERE CORYOSAURUS TYRANNOSAURUS REX

V

DAWN OF THE AGE OF REPTILES

FOR most of us, the word "reptile" has unpleasant connotations. We think of the creatures that bear the name as beings of a very low order. And so, in a certain sense, they are. But the time was when the creatures of which present-day reptiles are, so to say, but a degraded remnant, were the aristocrats of the earth. They were not only higher than any organic beings theretofore evolved, but apparently they represented the very peak of the evolutionary process. At that time—which compassed a stretch of perhaps three hundred million years —the reptiles might well have been supposed (had an inquiring mind been there to do the supposing) to be the climactic representatives of the ideal toward which the evolutionary process had been shaping living organisms for something like two billions of years.

As to that estimate, everything depends on the point of view. In any event, it is interesting to reflect that we have now come to the period of Mother Earth's history at which these strange creatures are beginning to make play for ascendancy. The story of their upward struggle and age-long triumph is not without its spectacular elements.

Not that there was anything spectacular about the first representatives of the tribe, there at the opening of the Mesozoic Era—the first period of which is known as the Triassic. Their ancestry was nothing to boast of, the founder of their Order being a lowly amphibian that had

AGE OF REPTILES, JURASSIC PERIOD

not got on in the world. He was not one of the higher Amphibians that had come to a dominant position in the world during the Carboniferous period (and had then gone into a decline, like the aristocrats of other sub-kingdoms), but a poor relation, of whom nothing much had ever been expected.

But now history was repeating itself, for the descendants of the erstwhile poor relation were by way of ousting the haughtiest of the Amphibian clan — not by actual extermination of the race, but by suppression of its aristocracy in true proletariat fashion. Soon there was no amphibian left that dared challenge the supremacy of an average representative of even a moderately evolved Order of the commonwealth of Reptiles. And presently there were reptiles abroad that so far surpassed in size and rapacity any living thing that had hitherto inhabited the globe that they may well have appeared to their Arthropod, Molluscan, and Amphibian contemporaries as god-like beings from another planet.

Even in the Triassic period, which occupied only the first hundred million years of the era, there were Dinosaurs that stalked along the mud-flats of what in future would be the valley of the Connecticut River, leaving three-toed, bird-like tracks upward of sixteen inches in length. And the creature that made this sizable imprint on the muds of time—an imprint which at that period probably established a world-record—was but a pigmy in comparison with the actual giants of the race that were to come a few-score millions of years later. Indeed, the Dinosaurs of this early period perhaps did not greatly surpass the Amphibians that still struggled to maintain a foothold—since some of these attained a length of fifteen or twenty feet.

But of course mere size is not everything—tho it was

DUCK-BILLED AND OSTRICH DINOSAURS

pretty nearly everything in the society of that period. The fact could never be forgotten that even the lordliest Amphibian was only half modern, since the first part of its life was spent under water, breathing like a fish; whereas every reptile was an air-breather, and nothing but an air-breather, from the moment it left the shell. Distinctions like that speak for themselves.

It is true that some reptiles reverted to the water, and spent their lives there, but this was from choice, not necessity. These swimmers were fish-like only in habit. They were four-legged lung-breathers, with three-chambered hearts, and a bony framework hardly susceptible of improvement. If they exchanged paws for flippers, and spike-tails for fish-tails, it was because these types of mechanisms had been proved the best possible for aquatic locomotion. When in Rome, do as the Romans do. It is a sign that you are progressive — that your race belongs to the future—if you are able to adapt yourself to new conditions. To conquer the land, and then to go back into the sea and outmaster the fishes at their own game, is a feat to boast of.

A far greater feat, however, was accomplished by the members of another new branch of the Reptile order, which was developed presently. I mean the conquest of the air. No trilobite, no cephalopod, no amphibian ever dreamed of such an accomplishment. No fish ever attempted it except in the most tentative fashion. Yet here was a reptile that found water and earth too narrow a habitat, and aspired to go up into the air, after the manner of certain recently developed small-fry called Insects.

Success, says a modern practical philosopher, is conditioned on ambition, imagination, and the will to work. A reptile that aspired to fly certainly did not lack am-

EARLIEST KNOWN BIRD (ARCHEOPTERYX)
FROM JURASSIC

bition. It had at least a serviceable substitute for imagination. The sequel proved that it—and its descendants to the ten-millionth generation — had the will to work. Doubtless ambition and will were fortified by the sight of large-mouthed confrères coming at it with greed in their eyes. Something more or less akin to that is the spur to most creative efforts. Sweet are the uses of adversity.

Motivation and extraneous aids aside, note the sequel. In time, a descendant of the ambitious reptile took the air. We pass over the million tentatives—the slightly sagging flap of skin that buoyed one up a little, and made a longer leap possible; the wider skin-flap that permitted tentative soaring—and hail the arrival of Pterosaur, the reptile that can really fly. Or at least can soar effectively, like the forerunner of all gliding machines. However you phrase it, here was a creature that progressed through the air. A small creature individually; yet the forerunner of flying reptiles with a wing-spread of twenty feet.

First vertebrate voyager of the air. Prototype of birds and bats—and airplanes. Even had the reptiles of the Triassic no other claim to distinction, this is an imperishable record.

In reality, however, the development of the flying mechanism was by no means the greatest achievement of Evolution in the Triassic. The blue ribbon event was something altogether different. Higher — incomparably higher—distinction goes to another branch of the reptile order, which (having neither ambition, imagination, nor the will to work for guidance), developed, in the course of inconceivable generations, a four-chambered heart that divided the two circulations and gave its possessor warm blood. To cap the climax, this creature also acquired the unimaginably novel capacity to suckle its young.

BRONTOSAURUS, LARGEST OF PREHISTORIC
REPTILES

When these miracles—they were no less than that—had been accomplished, the aforetime reptiles thus strangely departing from ancestral structure and custom were no longer reptiles. They were creatures of a new Order — primordial Mammals. Contemporary intelligence, had it attained human standards, would have adjudged the warm-blooded, milk-giving creature a monstrosity.

A monstrosity it was, in a sense; an abnormal being, deformed in structure and aberrant of function, according to all antecedent racial standards. And foredoomed, one might predict, to early extinction. For how could a creature born so helpless as to require maternal attention hope to compete with creatures that jump alertly from the shell and seek their own food?

But such auguries, however natural, would have been as futile as most auguries are and have ever been. In the abnormalities of form and function of that little monstrosity lay all the potentialities of mammalian progress —through monotreme and marsupial and early placental to dog and horse and ape and man. Of course many millions of generations were to pass before those potentialities became secure realities. In this Triassic period, and for scores of millions of years to come, the descendants of the little warm-blooded milk-guzzler would be but cowering outcasts, too insignificant to attract even passing notice from the gigantic lordlings that continue to dominate earth, sea, and sky, in what long remained the Age of Reptiles.

FLYING DRAGON (*PTERANODON*) AND
WINGLESS BIRD

VI

THE FOUR-CHAMBERED HEART AND
WHAT CAME OF IT

IN speaking of the evolvement of the first mammal, incidental mention was made of the invention of a four-chambered heart. An event of such significance must not be passed over thus casually. The four-chambered heart was a device ranking with the vertebral column and the air-filtering lungs among the very greatest inventions of all time. The thin septum of tissue that was formed across the ventricle chamber of a reptilian heart, and divided it into two chambers, was, judged by its consequences, one of the three or four most important structures ever devised in the whole course of evolution.

The obscure little Triassic reptile whose heart bore that device was the Adam of all the warm-blooded races of the future—the direct ancestor of every bird and mammal; the potential conqueror of the earth. Which once more illustrates the value of little things—the *right* little things, in the right place.

What this particular little device did was to prevent the two kinds of blood that came to the heart from immediately intermingling. In the old three-chambered heart — which every reptile still wears — the oxygen-laden blood from the lungs and the carbon-dioxid-vitiated blood from the body tissues in general, were mixed together in the one ventricle, and passed almost indifferently to either aorta. So there could be no sharp dis-

UNEARTHING A FOSSIL

ASSEMBLING A SKELETON,
AMERICAN MUSEUM OF NATURAL HISTORY

tinction between arterial and venous blood. The blood pumped through the left aorta to the body-tissues was of much the same quality as that pumped through the right aorta to the lungs for oxygenation.

Under such conditions, the chemical process of oxidation in the cellular tissues, a basic essential of the life-process, must be relatively sluggish. The attendant liberation of heat would be correspondingly restricted. And the blood thus inadequately heated would be further cooled by admixture with lung-cooled blood in the ventricular chamber. A creature with this defective circulatory equipment would, so to say, live slowly, be relatively sluggish in action, and have a body temperature but little higher than that of its surroundings.

It is true that under certain conditions these handicaps may not be so serious as they sound. "Relative" sluggishness may not bar exceedingly quick movements on occasion, as the activities of a fish will testify. And there may be distinct advantages, for a creature living in a very warm atmosphere or, contrariwise, in very cold water, in having tissues adapted to functioning under surrounding conditions of temperature, whether high or low. Which goes to show—if again we must moralize—that bad things are not always so bad, nor good things always so good, as they may seem.

That superfluous moralization, however, does not cancel the estimate of the four-chambered heart—which gave true arterial blood, increased activation of tissues, and laid the foundation for a self-heated body—as a mechanism of inestimable importance in determining progression from the reptilian stage of existence to what, from the human viewpoint (tho perhaps not from the reptilian), seems the higher plane of life of bird and mammal.

Yet it cannot be denied that the handicap element must have made itself felt rather urgently to the early descendants of the little reptile of the four-chambered heart. For the continent of their habitation was moving perennially northward, slowly, to be sure, but effectively. And the sun does not shine so genially year in and year out at, say, thirty degrees north latitude as it did when you were basking under the equator—notwithstanding the loathness of certain modern interpreters of geologic history to recognize that truism.

At the equator, for example, the midday sun is never more than twenty-three and a half degrees from the zenith. At the thirtieth parallel of latitude, the midday sun in mid-winter is *fifty-three and a half* degrees from the zenith. Do you note the difference? You may be certain that the little warm-blooded pro-mammal noticed it.

But what could be done about it? That was the important question. There are to be various answers. It seemed desirable that this exceedingly interesting experiment with super-reptiles should go on, and Evolution is a very resourceful *Deus ex machina*. After all, the obstacle was no greater than sundry others that had already been overcome.

A half-hearted solution might be found in having the warm-blooded super-reptile go into retirement during the season when the sun went too far away. Some of the old-fashioned amphibians and reptiles were learning to do that—and were to continue to let this makeshift expedient suffice for all time. Witness the hibernation of frogs, snakes, and turtles in our own day. Warm-bloods can do the same, with the right training, as woodchucks, gophers, and even bears were ultimately to prove. But on the whole such a begging of the question would

THE PROTEROCERATOPS OF ANDREWS

hardly answer for a creature that specialized in activity rather than in reptilian dormancy.

Another possible expedient would be to follow the sun (as far as the southern border of the continent permitted), and thus live in perpetual summer-land. But this would be practically feasible for only the small contingent of reptiles that had learned to fly—and the new warm-bloods were not of that branch of the family. Moreover, following the sun would involve having the entire population in one region at the same time, which was hardly an economic practicality. So migration, albeit a useful accessory expedient, no more solved the main problem than would hibernation.

The remaining expedient was to set to work to develop a protective covering for the new creature, by which its self-generated furnace could be prevented from radiating its heat too rapidly into space. Here, indeed, was a task worthy of Evolution at its best. Protective coverings were, indeed, no novelty. All manner of such had been developed, to shield their possessors from contusion and from the attacks of their enemies. So it had been abundantly proved that the integument of an organism may be made to assume strange forms and qualities—from chitinous or calcareous shells of invertebrates to scales of fishes and bony plates of Dinosaurs. But the covering now called for was of a new order. It need not give protection in the old sense, because these warm-blooded creatures would be active enough to escape their enemies. Its essential function would be to conserve heat.

Fertile in expedients, as always, Evolution set to work along several lines, and before you could say Jack Robinson—that is to say, in the course of the short hundred million years from mid-Triassic to mid-Jurassic time—

she had solved the problem not once merely, but twice. And each solution was a veritable triumph. For one of the new heat-conserving mantles of modified integument was *Fur*—and the other was *Feathers*. The two tribes of descendants of the reptilian Adam of the four-chambered heart might well feel that now the world was their oyster.

Say, rather, that each one of these tribes might feel that the world was *its* oyster; for of course the two had meantime diverged so far in various directions that cousinship would no longer be admitted by either. The matter of common origin was forgotten. No longer would any old-school reptile admit relationship with either of the newcomers, for that matter. The fur-bearers and feather-bearers, with heretical hot blood, could be regarded only as degenerate and despicable offshoots of a noble race. Even to let them retain the honored name of their ancestors would be a travesty.

And the latter part of this verdict, at least, seems justified. So the fur-bearers were to rank as founders of the new class of Mammals; and the feather-bearers as the progenitors of another new class, the Birds.

For a time it may well have seemed that the birds were the superior product of this mighty experiment in evolution. Their great natural agility was accentuated by the support given by feathers that grew more and more profusely on their front legs, and a double row of plumes along the sides of the long reptilian tail that was still retained. Meantime the long horny jaws, with ample equipment of socketed teeth, served as an admirable weapon of offense and defense. The feathered creatures had long since adopted the bipedal locomotion of certain of the Dinosaurs, and hence had well developed their hind-legs, while the fore-legs, tho still supplied with clutching toes, had gradually changed their form, for better support of the rows of feathers which were proving of incalculable aid in running, hopping, and soaring.

In course of time, the muscles of the chests were strengthened by use and developed through heredity, and now they could make the feather-bearing fore-limbs beat the air so effectively as to lift the creature from the ground and propel it through the air, in emu-lation of the best-flying of reptiles. Through another series of evolutionary changes, the long reptilian tail was discarded, or abbreviated into a stubby affair, on which the tail-feathers were aggregated into a fan.

Now, indeed, the erstwhile reptile had become a Bird, in the full sense of the word as after-ages were to in-terpret it. Save only that teeth were retained, in socket or groove, it was a bird of "modern" type. Away back there in the Age of Reptiles, this feathered creature had attained practical perfection of form and function. Too close an approximation, in one view, for there seemed no excuse for further evolutionary experiment.

So the bird, by the very success of its early develop-ment, shut itself off from further development. Minor modifications were to occur, as we shall see; but in all essentials the bird of the later Mesozoic era—the Age of Reptiles—was a perfected mechanism, come thus early to the limits of useful specialization. It would ever re-main an egg-laying super-reptile; while the fur-bearer, which at first seemed inferior, was to cast off the rep-tilian habit of egg-laying, and was to go on in succeed-ing ages, through a series of evolutionary experiments, to progressions culminating (for the present) in such diversified organisms as shrews and elephants, bats and whales, porcupines and armadillos, kangaroos and men.

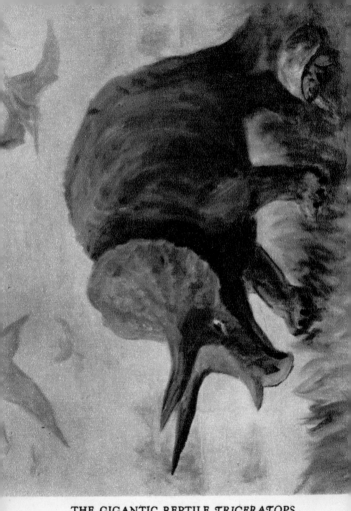

THE GIGANTIC REPTILE *TRICERATOPS*

VII

THE SIERRA NEVADA REVOLUTION

WHAT manner of environment was it into which these Jurassic precursors of birds and men were born, there in Holarctica? Let us attempt to envisage it. The same vast stretch of territory that we saw in Paleozoic time still varied in contour, but was in general of higher elevation, especially along the central axis. The thickened terrain makes the oscillations—inevitable in a floating raft-mass of such extent—of wider sweep and of somewhat less rapid change. The central area of what will be the eastern United States is well above water, suffering erosion, but receiving scant strata-forming deposits. The eroded material from the Appalachians is being deposited to the east. There the land that will be Europe is for the most part submerged, giving subterranean foothold for myriads of invertebrate creatures that, millennium after millennium, are adding their quota to the work of rock-building.

Western North America also has an area of submergence, a great geosyncline that marks the future Sierra Nevada location. Here sediment comes from both east and west—that is to say, from future North America and Asia. There is also a shallower sea stretching across the future Rocky Mountain region. This sea will persist, with intervals of recession, into a later period (the Cretaceous). Then, broken into flood-plains, it will become one of the most marvelous repositories for the remains of animal life to be found anywhere on the globe.

For of course it is only under water that animal or vegetable organisms are preserved as fossils, just as new strata of rocks (originally silt or sand and organic débris) are formed there. So, rather paradoxically, the regions that at a future period will be registered as "Jurassic" are precisely the regions where now there is no land visible. The actual land surface across which we are looking will be marked on geological maps of the future as showing no Jurassic formations.

It is a surface covered in the main with vegetation of tropical luxuriance. If the great club-mosses have disappeared, there is in their place a jungle of ferns, equisetæ, and colossal conifers. Some of the latter are eight feet in diameter, almost rivaling the California redwoods of a later day. There are countless cycads also, with palm-like foliage. Some of these are sixty or eighty feet in height. They are notable not only in themselves, but because they are to become the progenitors of the great group of Angiosperms, or flowering plants, not yet in evidence, but in future to be the dominant vegetation of the earth.

There are no grasses or cereals, but neither are there mammals that need such vegetation for forage. The members of the dominant reptilian population are largely carnivorous in habit; or if herbivorous, are of such physical proportions that they browse on the foliage of all but the tallest trees. Incredible as it may seem, there are hosts of these reptiles that dwarf a modern elephant in bulk, and stretch up necks that make the reach of a giraffe seem Lilliputian. Here, for example, stalking across a marshy stretch of future Utah, is a Sauropod (*Diplodocus*) that is more than a hundred feet in length. It is a short-legged creature, as you see, in proportion to its length. In actuality, its thigh-bones are seven feet long. Fortunately it has no evil intent, being bent on securing for its dinner a few hundred pounds of vegetable matter only.

Equally innocuous, probably, if unmolested, is yonder Stegosaur, despite its forty-foot carcass and vast armament of jagged dorsal plates and tail-spines. And that twenty-five-foot Triceratops, twice the bulk of an elephant, wears its eight-foot helmet-skull and three extraordinary rhinoceros-horns likewise for protection, not as weapons of offense, tho the very sight of them is terrifying.

Such defensive armors would never have been developed had they not been needed, you may be sure. Evolution does not carry such experiments in protective coverings much beyond the actual needs of the moment. It is too costly an equipment for that—costly in terms of energy and impairment of activity. Creatures so handicapped must be of excessively sluggish movement, incapable of adapting themselves to ever-so-slight a change in the food-conditions of their environment. We do not need to be told that they will inevitably become extinct in the relatively near future, when the Holarctica of their habitation moves on a little farther to the north, out of the equatorial belt where alone vegetation can flourish luxuriantly enough to furnish nourishment for such colossal carcasses.

In the meantime, however, the great reptiles had no alternative to the development of their grotesque but effective armaments, if they would live and perpetuate their species, even for a few million years. For there are other reptiles abroad that feed on flesh—creatures, some of them, no less Brobdingnagian, with predatory equipment proportionate to their size, and of a ferocity fully in keeping. *Tyrannosaurus rex,* for instance, king of all

TYRANNOSAURUS REX, LARGEST FLESH-EATING
REPTILE

the tyrant saurians (Therapod Dinosaurs), forty-odd feet in length, with the jaws of a steam-shovel—to be famed in future as being "in respect to speed, size, power, and ferocity the most destructive life engine which has ever been evolved" (Osborn).

It would be worth a long journey to see a gladiatorial contest (from the coign of vantage of an airplane) between this king of the Tyrannosaurs and a triple-horned Ceratops of the armored head. But, alas! Those days are gone forever. The king of the Therapods, no less than the giant tribes that were his meal-ticket, was doomed by the very over-specialization that made him the unchallenged autocrat of his era. He and all the tribes of his confrères, save a few insignificant turtles, lizards, crocodiles, and degenerate snakes (the last of which did not appear till the close of the era), were destined to pass from the scene before the close of the age to which they gave their name.

For the moment, however, here in the Jurassic period, at the middle of the Mesozoic era, there is nothing to suggest so gloomy an augury. This is indeed the Age of Reptiles. Who could doubt that it would last forever? It would be a pessimistic judgment, indeed, that would predict its early overthrow. Yet we who view it in retrospect know that it could not conceivably last. The northward drift of Holarctica, under stress of the urge for geoid balance, could not be stayed. And the climatic changes that must attend this shift of geographical location could by no possibility be tolerated by these cold-blooded children of the sun.

Yet it was not climatic change alone that was the nemesis of the great saurians. There were other continents than Holarctica to which some of them made their way (just how they got there we shall inquire before we are through), where climatic conditions long remained favorable. But even there their fate was no less certain, tho perhaps delayed. The real nemesis of the saurians was over-specialization along purely physical lines. They developed brawn, but signally failed to develop brain. And they held to their faulty three-chambered hearts, and attendant cold blood and sluggishness of reaction.

The time was to come, inevitably, when their despised poor-relations of the furred coats, four-chambered hearts, and tissues fed with well oxygenated blood, were to prove also specialists in the development of *brains*—and *there* was a combination that was predestined to conquer the world. Alertness, speed, quick-thinking, adaptability were to take the place of mere physical power as guarantors of success in the struggle for existence.

VIII

CHALK-MAKING EXTRAORDINARY

THE life of the great reptiles was to go on for about two hundred million years thereafter, not greatly changed, except that one race after another dwindled, until its last member fell by the wayside, as the slowly changing climatic conditions introduced new food problems that the highly specialized creatures could not master. But meantime there were other tribes of organisms, including the newly evolved mammals and birds, that thrived abundantly. These found life-conditions more and more propitious, somewhat in proportion to the reduction of the hitherto dominant reptilian population.

There were multitudes of birds now that had completely mastered the art of flying—birds mostly no larger than a pigeon, but diversified in form, to the extent of constituting varied species, and so alert and swift of wing as to be able to evade capture, for the most part, by any existing enemy whomsoever. These flying birds of the Cretaceous period still had teeth, but in other respects they were of thoroughly "modern" aspect, exemplifying the amazing power of Evolution to develop a mechanism so utterly different from the ancestral reptilian form, in a relatively brief period— for hardly more than a hundred million years had elapsed since the time of the lizard-tailed pro-birds of the Jurassic. More remarkable still, perhaps, from another angle, was the fact that a creature that had come so far in so short a time should now pause, as if at the apex of perfection, and remain static, ignored seemingly by the spirit of progress, for all the future.

Meantime there were other birds that had developed along lines far different—as regards important details, not essentials of structure. These were haunters of the water, who had not acquired—or, having acquired, had lost afterward—the power of flight. These birds had somewhat the aspect of the modern loon, but some of them were upward of six feet in length. The auks and penguins were to be their closest representatives at a later era, but those remote descendants would lack the reptilian teeth that armed the jaws of the great feathered divers of the Cretaceous.

A six-foot bird, swimming like a fish, must have been able to take care of itself under ordinary conditions. But conditions were not "ordinary" in the Cretaceous seas, any more than on the land surfaces or the interior lagoons of the period. What chance had even a six-foot bird against the reptilian tribes called *Ichthyosaurs* (because they had become so fish-like), which were often twenty-five or thirty feet long; or the veritable sea-serpent reptiles called *Mosasaurs*, which stretched their agile serpentine bodies to a length of upward of seventy-five feet? How could any young *Hesperornis* (flightless bird) ever grow to maturity in the midst of such uncongenial associates? Mostly they could not, presumably; which in part accounts for the extinction of the birds of this order. That argument tends to lose force, however, when we reflect that the flying birds (*Ichthyornis*) of the period were also to become extinct, in the sense that they left no descendants that were not sufficiently modified to be appraised by classifiers of the future as of new *Orders*.

There were hosts of families that thus came to an end (the traditions of their ancestry carried on only by collateral branches) in this Cretaceous period, here toward the close of the Age of Reptiles. But so, for that matter, there had been in every antecedent period since organic life began. Only, the conspicuousness of the great Saurians made their demise the more spectacular. The extinction of a tribe of hundred-foot Dinosaurs certainly has greater news value than the blotting out of a tribe of, let us say, marine Ammonites, which by no chance could ever have made the front page, even in their prime.

Yet in a broad view the unspectacular marine creatures must be adjudged far more important citizens of the Mesozoic commonwealth than the boisterous reptiles that imposed their name on the Era. The Ammonites just referred to, for example, not merely outnumbered the Saurians millions to one as individuals, but exceeded them hundreds to one in species; and their calcareous shells built up thousands of feet of stony strata in the sea-beds (subsequently to be raised to continental heights), while the bones of all the reptiles together, scattered across a similar area, would have added but a film to the structure of the land-mass.

These Ammonites were mollusks, housed snail-like in shells, which sometimes attained a size of several feet. There were thousands of species, and they could boast a direct ammonoid ancestry somewhat more remote than the reptilian ancestry of any Saurian. But, like the reptiles, they were now fallen on evil days, toward the close of the Cretaceous. The changing temperature of the water, perhaps, was among the new conditions that failed to meet their approval. They struggled, however, to adapt themselves to the altering conditions, and for a time appeared to succeed. But the coilings and ram's-horn twistings of shell that now began to characterize them told not of real progress, but rather of degeneration. And as they became more and more fantastic, they were in effect only making what might be termed "death-contortions" (Agassiz). The close of the era was to witness their final elimination—a phenomenon, it may be added, which has been characterized as one of the most sudden and abrupt terminations of a great and abundant race in the history of organic life. But "sudden and abrupt" must here be interpreted in a geologic sense, of course. A geologic "cataclysm" may involve many millions of years.

There were thousands of other marine organisms that suffered a like fate. That was inevitable at this stage of continental progress, for now the northern border of Holarctica was passing beyond the subtropical zone. A multitude of marine forms, including many corals, must of necessity perish, through inability to adapt themselves to the gradually chilling waters of higher latitudes.

There were yet other marine creatures, however, that thrived and developed under the new conditions. Notable among these were certain single-celled organisms (Protozoans) known as Foraminifers and Radiolarians, which peopled the waters in inconceivable abundance. These are creatures that might be said to be timeless, since they were among the very earliest of living organisms, and their descendants exist not greatly modified in the oceans of our own day. But in the Cretaceous period the foraminifers in particular took on a new lease of life, and proliferated to an unprecedented extent. They crowded the waters in such incredible numbers that their tiny shells, showered down on the sea-beds, built up what in after time would be known as the chalk-beds that are today so significant a feature of the coasts of England (at Dover, for example), and France, and of the Gulf Coast of the United States.

It was because of the prominence of these chalk-beds, especially in England and France, where William Smith, the father of stratigraphic geology, gained the clue to the fossil-secrets by their study, that the name Cretaceous (from the Latin *Creta*, chalk) was given to the great period which terminated the Age of Reptiles. The phrase "Age of Reptiles," however, is only a nickname for the era technically known as the Mesozoic; whereas "Cretaceous" is the accepted technical, no less than popular, designation for the period covering about two hundred and fifty million years, and represented by a maximum depth of hardly less than six miles of rocky strata.

By no means all the rocks of these strata are chalk, to be sure; but they all bear the name "Cretaceous." So the work of the tiny foraminifer has received recognition in technical annals that insures this obscure protozoan a permanency of fame outmatching that of the king of the Dinosaurs and his colossal confrères.

UNEARTHING A DINOSAUR — VARNISHING DAY

IX

THE ROCKY MOUNTAIN REVOLUTION

ON a great continent-raft like Holarctica, afloat on
a globe of unevenly curved surface, something
important was always happening—and something rather
more important was always about to happen. One of
the things always happening, as we have seen, was the
warping of the sial-substance of the continent, under
stress of gravitation-pull and inertia-thrust. The simple
principle of buoyancy demanded that the continent-
mass should settle to a certain depth into the supporting
sima (with its overlying film of ocean)—the depth at
which, when equilibrium was established, the amount
of sima displaced would just equal the mass of the sial
continent as a whole. (The "principle of Archimedes.")

But that ideal could be attained only if the continent
remained stationary both as to position and as to mass.
And of course it did neither. It constantly shifted its
location, and as constantly changed its outline (in minor
degree) and its surface contour.

The basal remnant of the aforetime Taconic and
Appalachian ranges, which stretched transversely across
a considerable breadth of Holarctica in one location,
and the remnant of the Sierra Nevada range somewhat
parallel a few thousand miles to the west, were ultimately to exercise an important influence in determining the lines of fracture through which Holarctica
would be riven into three segments. The central segment, to be known as North America, would be vir-

tually framed by the two systems of mountain-bases in question.

That some such fragmentation of the far-flung Holarctic land-raft must ultimately occur was obviously inevitable, if the northward drift continued. The eastern and western borders of the continent, lying ten thousand miles apart across the land surface, and therefore separated in the other direction by fourteen thousand miles of water (the remaining circuit of the globe at the equator), must be brought progressively nearer together as the northern latitude-circles become smaller and smaller in circumference.

A lateral segment of Holarctica at the equator would have somewhat the form of an unstrung bow. The same segment, as the continent drifts northward, must have the form of a bow increasingly bent. Neither bow nor continent can bend beyond a certain point without breaking. Short of that point, the elasticity of the bow, and the elasticity-plus-crumpling of the continent, permit bending without actual fracture. In the Cretaceous period, at which the Holarctica of our observation has arrived, the center of the continent had as yet passed only about thirty-five degrees beyond the equator, and the warping involved was still susceptible of adjustment by flexure and mountain-upheaval. But the time was imminent when such makeshifts would no longer suffice. One more great local adjustment was to be made, however, involving the central part of the continent, before the final catastrophe. That adjustment was being prepared for in the latter part of the Cretaceous period —the Age of little Foraminifers that made chalk, and great Dinosaurs that terrorized the land—in a stretch of territory lying at the east of the recently-formed Sierra Nevada range of mountains.

Here changing conditions were speeding up the evolutionary process. Here, sequentially, perhaps the greatest of local upheavals of strata hitherto occurring in Holarctica would evidence the last gigantic—even tho hopelessly ineffectual—effort at preservation of continental integrity.

It was during the later million-year periods of the late Cretaceous time ("Upper Cretaceous," technically) that the great reptilian population of Holarctica was making its last stand. It has been said that Time fought against them. But this must not be taken in too literal a sense, for we cannot be sure that there is any time-limit on the existence of races of living organisms. The history of primitive forms that survive from the Pale-ozoic seems to suggest the contrary. But what *does* fight against every highly specialized race is Time's great concomitant, changing conditions. Changing conditions of topography and climate. Changing conditions of food supply, of competition in securing sustenance, of jeopardy from enemies.

Here in the great terrain that in future would be western America—in the very heart of one of the favorite resorts of the great Dinosaurs—there were changes of topography that in themselves must have cost the lives of millions of reptiles of high and low degree. The warping of the distraught continent brought vast areas below sea level, destroying forests of cycads and conifers, and doubtless the larger part of the sluggish land population. Only creatures of exceptional agility, like the little mammals and birds, were likely to escape—and these only when the inundation took place very gradually.

The sinking of land on the whole was progressive, so that detritus and organic remains ultimately attained a thickness of many thousands of feet, even as measured in terms of compacted rock-strata. Yet there were periods of oscillation, or perhaps of general lowering of sea-level, which brought local areas again above water. These would be repopulated, and then again suffer submergence. There were numberless lagoons and lakes and flood plains that thus alternated as land and water surfaces, on the whole subsiding fast enough to permit perennial deposit of materials for future rock-strata.

In some regions, conditions were favorable for accumulations of vegetable waste that became compacted into beds of lignite, resembling the coal-beds of the ancient Carboniferous period. Even the northern border of the continent was still in the temperate zone, and a newer type of vegetation was being evolved that could thrive outside the tropics. Conifers had become abundant (the Genus *Sequoia,* still represented in the modern world by the Big Tree and Redwood of California, appeared at about this epoch), and for a time had given promise of dominance in the vegetable world, comparable to that of great reptiles among animals. But now the new types of flowering plants (Angiosperms) were forging ahead— and their promise of early and permanent supremacy was not fallacious.

Many of the new plants were of such "modern" type that they might be recognized as progenitors of palms, oaks, maples, tulip-trees, and figs. There were grasses, too, and a multitude of herbaceous plants, adapted for the grazing and browsing of the small herbivorous mammals that were increasing as the reptilian population declined.

Most of these flowering plants depended for their racial existence on a strange "symbiosis," or coalition, with members of the recently-evolved tribe of flying insects. They developed nectar-bearing receptacles in connection with their procreative organs (which in turn were transformed leaves), and supplemented these with whorls of leaves transformed into colored "petals," as a further insect-guide to the food-supply. The insects, feeding on the nectar, would unconsciously reciprocate by transferring pollen from one flower to another, thus accomplishing a cross-fertilization that had been found exceedingly advantageous in furthering the evolutionary process. Two parents are better than one, because each parent has developed in response to its environment some qualities that the other lacks, and the offspring may inherit qualities which, in combination, will make it superior to either parent. Plants of low orders have motile sperm-cells, to accomplish such cross-fertilization. Some higher plants depend on the wind to convey their pollen. But the device of seeking the cooperation of insects was a triumphant even if unwitting invention, as all the future was to demonstrate in perpetuity.

Yet the insects which from this time forward increased in number and variety till they outnumbered all other multicellular organisms, were by no means an unmixed blessing. They harassed even the mightiest vertebrates by direct attack, and became inadvertent transmitters of bacterial germs that could flourish extravagantly if they gained admission to the blood-stream of a higher animal. These bacteria, among the very earliest of living things to be evolved, had played an essential role in the organic world—fixing nitrogen from the air for plant-food; causing the decomposition of dead tissues, for further support of plant life, which in turn is the support of animal life. Certain tribes of their clan had colonized living bodies, and established a sort of truce, whereby incredible hordes of them might thrive (say in an intestinal tract) while their host also thrived. (There

UINTATHERE, AN EOCENE MAMMAL

are more of them living in the intestinal tract of every human being, for example, than there have been human beings in the world since the beginning.)

But there are other tribes of bacteria that have not formed such a coalition, and which, if they do find opportunity to enter an animal organism, multiply so rapidly there as to imperil the life of their host. These are the so-called "germs of disease." They account for the death of countless individuals of most species of higher organisms. There is reason to believe that through their agency multitudes of species have been exterminated in the past. It is well within the probabilities that such bacterial invaders, aided now for the first time by insect carriers, may have constituted a new menace to the dominant reptiles of the Cretaceous period—another of the new conditions that called for adaptations (thickened skin, for example, particularly for juveniles) that perhaps could not be made in time to save the race.

Dangers of a different kind, but no less portentous, threatened from the unexpected direction of the activities of the newly-evolved little mammals and birds. These were creatures of seeming insignificance, from the standpoint, say, of the king of the Dinosaurs. Yet they were able to challenge the very existence of his race by attacking his offspring as they came from the shell, or by destroying the unguarded eggs themselves, which the mother Dinosaur must deposit in more or less exposed places, to get the benefit of the warmth of a sun that no longer shone with aforetime brightness. The growing intelligence of the mammals—whose brains increased in proportion age by age — enabled them better and better to circumvent any plans for egg-hiding that the stupid Dinosaurs might invent.

And so it may have come to pass, while Holarctica, at

least as to its southern portion, still lay in a zone where climatic conditions were not intolerable for the cold-blooded, sun-loving giants, that the last Dinosaur disappeared from that continent because of the depredations of a little fox-sized mammal, with fox-like intelligence, whose penchant for reptile eggs could not be checkmated.

That birds did not suffer a like fate was due to the fact that these modified lizards learned to build inaccessible cradles for their eggs, and to guard both eggs and fledglings with intelligent assiduity. Meantime there were doubtless species of birds that aided in the work of decimating the reptilian ranks, by indulging, in competition with the mammals, a penchant for eggs as articles of diet.

Without carrying the analysis farther, it is perhaps evident that there were reasons aplenty why the changing conditions of the world toward the close of this period were not conducive to further aggrandizement of the race of Reptiles that had attained such dominance in the preceding millennia. In any event, the decline of the Dinosaurs, and the ultimate extinction of thirteen Orders of Reptiles (out of eighteen that existed) throughout the wide territory of Holarctica before the close of the Cretaceous period, were epochal developments of world-history.

Some of the great Saurians managed to maintain existence for a somewhat longer period in certain regions of the southern hemisphere (e.g., Argentina), but there too they were doomed. Probably few of them were living at the time when physical conditions in Holarctica came to a "cataclysmic" upheaval that transformed the region of the sediment-trough east of the Sierra Nevadas into the colossal elevation of the Rocky Mountain region.

For so long a time—long even in the geological sense—had this region been a trough of deposit, tho subject to recurring interruptions, that the strata involved in this "Rocky Mountain Revolution," marking the termination of the Cretaceous, were not merely the accumulated twenty thousand feet of Mesozoic strata, but below that an even deeper formation (26,000 feet) of Paleozoic rocks, and below that, in turn, a yet greater deposit (30,-000 feet) that dated from the Proterozoic era. This constitutes "the longest accessible geological section known anywhere," and attests (in the words of Schuchert) "the striking fact that the earth's crust may subside at least 14 miles before it becomes folded into mountains."

The same spasmodic contortion that produced this vast Rocky Mountain upheaval brought about the elevation, to a height of two thousand or three thousand feet, of the Appalachian region, which had been worn to a peneplain almost at sea-level. Here the strata were not folded and contorted, but were pushed up with minimum disturbance of sequence, to form a vast dome—which the elements would at once begin carving into mountain-contours. Not the mountain-contours of the Appalachians of our day, of course, any more than the Rocky Mountain upheaval produced the mountain range that now occupies that region.

But in each case the upheaval, tho producing elevations that must soon be worn back toward the level, served to fortify the sial mass several miles beneath the surface, giving further assurance that when the final dismemberment of Holarctica became inevitable, this particular central segment would remain intact, to form by itself a substantial continent—North America.

BRONTOTHERE, AN OLIGOCENE MAMMAL

THE TERTIARY PERIOD

The Cenozoic Era, the newest era of the geological record, is divided into two Periods—the Tertiary, or "Age of Mammals," and the Quaternary, or "Age of Man." The Tertiary Period, which is the subject of the present section of this biography, is divided into four major Epochs, as follows:

Eocene Epoch	. . . . .	75,000,000 years
Oligocene "	. . . . .	75,000,000 "
Miocene "	. . . . .	75,000,000 "
Pliocene "	. . . . .	75,000,000 "

BELUCHITHERE, ELASMOTHERE
AND LIVING TAPIR

X

THE AGE OF EOHIPPUS

QUAINT little Eohippus! I speak of this first epoch of the Cenozoic Era—the Eocene epoch of the Tertiary period—as *his* age, not because he was the dominant animal of the time (far from it), but because he was the direct ancestor of the modern horse, man's great coadjutor for centuries in doing the world's work. Therefore he occupies a position of unique distinction in the scale of evolutionary history.

But for that matter, we should not go far wrong in starring little Eohippus on his own merits; or at least in connection with the story of his immediate descendants, even had his line led to less distinguished culmination. For he was among the earliest exemplifiers of a startling new experiment in evolution; the proponent of a new doctrine, if you wish to put it that way—a doctrine which taught that radical changes in plans of animal architecture might be highly advantageous; and taught, needless to say, not by pragmatism, but by example.

Behold, then, little Eohippus (pro-horse of the Eocene), here in the early part of Age of Mammals—not much bigger than a cat, yet a true horse in the making, and in token thereof bearing only four toes, instead of the traditional five, on each front foot. And on each rear foot, *only three toes!* And such toes! The mere number, after all, was not the chief point; for certain reptiles had long before set the three-toe example. (Indeed, Eohippus himself had a long line of ancestors

91

with only three toes on each hind foot.) But the peculiarity of these new toes was that the middle one on each foot was enlarged, so that it did chief service, leaving its mates as scarcely more than ornamental—or unornamental—appendages.

In reality, that big middle toe was a hoof in the making. It gave augury of a time when the other toes would disappear altogether (or with only residual traces left as "splints"), while the single useful toe, steadily enlarged and modified, would lose all semblance of a reptilian toe, or for that matter the toe of an ordinary mammal, and would rank, in the eye of the casual observer, as an entire foot (hoof).

Of course long evolutionary ages were ahead of little Eohippus before that dénouement; but, as was said, the end was forecast in the strange foot of the little Eocene mammal. And perhaps it is worth while to pause long enough to consider that strange—seemingly deformed—member somewhat in detail; not so much in the anatomical sense, as in relation to its evolutionary implications. The more so because this iconoclastic emblem was typical of other departures from tradition, whereby various distant cousins of Eohippus were proving themselves worthy representatives of a new and progressive era. The age of cold-blooded reptiles had passed; the age of warm-blooded mammals was at hand.

The old order had singularly changed. All the gigantic beasts of the preceding era had disappeared from the earth. The reptilian hordes that had dominated the world for millions of years had left only a few puny descendants, destined to occupy an utterly subordinate position for all time to come. The warm-blooded creatures that had learned to shelter their offspring within their bodies, and to suckle them after birth, were the dominant race—the most highly evolved organisms that had ever lived.

Yet at the beginning of the era, there was no member of the Mammalian clan that was larger than a modern sheep. In size, the new masters of creation were insignificant. The largest of them would have been but a morsel in the mouth of a reptilian giant of yore—or for that matter in the mouth of any one of a galaxy of gigantic fishes of the contemporary period. There were sharks sixty or eighty feet long in the waters, with teeth five or six inches across. A whole drove of little Eohippi would have been required to ration one of these monsters.

But tho their bodies were small, the little mammals had relatively big brains. That was the secret of their success. On the other hand, there was no direct connection between the brain-size and the future development of body-size of these creatures, any more than there had been in the case of their forerunners, the giant reptiles with little brains. Some gigantic mammals would in time be developed, with brains not very much above the reptilian standard. But in the sequel, these giants would always disappear before the advance of other allied animals that had developed bigger brains. So in the last analysis the big brains do count in the evolutionary scale. The qualification is made only to guard against the assumption that there is direct causal relation between increasing body-size and increasing brain-size. Nearly the largest brain ever developed is the endowment of a relatively small mammal called man.

In any event, our major concern of the moment is not with the brain but with the feet of little Eohippus. We wish to inquire by what process the little iconoclast has shuffled off the superfluous toes, and by what further

EXTINCT GROUND SLOTH AND, ABOVE,
MODERN SLOTH

process his descendants will continue the shuffling, till only a single toe to each foot remains. And in so doing, we hope to envisage the principles involved in similar processes of departure along other lines, followed by different groups of remote cousins of the little pro-horse. The camel family, for example, who finally compromised on two toes. Or the cats, who developed extraordinary claws. Or the whales, who exchanged their toes for flippers, and even, as regards the posterior equipment, dispensed with them altogether, and with legs as well.

In a word, we wish briefly to inspect the evolutionary process in practical operation. We would view a slow-motion movie of the transformation of one species into another. Naturally we are not seeking *ultimate* explanations of anything. Our concern is with the proximal causes and tangible manifestations that biological studies have revealed as certainties or as the most plausible hypotheses.

Briefly, then, the basic fact that underlies the evolutionary process is the fundamental law of heredity, according to which every creature tends to transmit to its progeny its own characteristics.

Offhand, that might seem to be a formula implying fixity of species, rather than mutation. But a moment's consideration reveals the joker. All higher organisms procreate by the union of sexes. Every new being is the offspring of *two* parents; and the parents are never identical, and may have opposing characteristics. One parent, for example, may have blue eyes and the other black; or one may be tall and the other short.

Obviously, a compromise is in order. The compromise may consist in the predominance, in the new generation, of one trait at the expense of the other; or in a blending of traits. The child of tall and short parents may be tall like one parent, or short like the other; or it may be of intermediate stature.

But let us go a step farther. Consider the next generation. The child that "took after" its father, and was short, may have offspring that appear to "take after" their grandmother, who was tall. A trait submerged in one generation has reappeared atavistically. This phenomenon is familiar to everyone. The scientific interpretation of the phenomenon was the work of the Austrian priest, Mendel. He showed that, where opposing traits are in question, the one that is suppressed in the first generation (called a "recessive" factor) will reappear in one individual in four, on the average, in the second generation.

If, for example, a black guinea-pig of pure strain is mated with a white guinea-pig of pure strain, all the offspring will be black; blackness(in this case) being "dominant." But in the next generation one individual in four will be as white as its grandmother—not only white in appearance, but absolutely without any factor for blackness in its germ plasm.

This basic phenomenon, totally unsuspected before the experiments of Mendel were made (and long afterward ignored), is of tremendous significance in its bearing on the problem of the evolution of new animal species that we are considering. It enables Evolution (if I may again use the convenient language of personification) to experiment in an amazing manner, and in the end to cast aside what has proved unuseful, and to hold fast to that which is good. ("Good," of course, meaning, what is useful for the race.)

The secret (at least according to the present writer's long-ago-published interpretation) is that the trait which is "dominant" in heredity (black hair in case of the guinea-pig) is the *newer* trait of the opposing pair; that is to say, the one more recently acquired. So this trait is given a hearing in the next generation, on the chance that it may be an improvement. But lest it be not an improvement, the old trait is recalled in the next generation, and retested, in competition with the new trait. And this procedure goes on generation after generation. Pure dominants and pure recessives are produced, along with individuals of mixed tendencies (like the black guinea-pigs of the first generation, which had in their germ plasm the factors for white also), until finally one type or another proves—by the acid test of increasing numbers—its superiority; and the other types, conversely, decrease in number or disappear altogether.

It must be further explained—and this point also is of salient significance—that only traits of comparatively recent origin, in racial history, will thus Mendelize. It is only these, indeed, that give opportunity for Mendelizing, because the fundamental characteristics of any species are the uniform endowment of every individual member of that species. These fundamental traits represent the accumulated experiments of millions of past generations—heredity being, as some one has said, the sum of past environments. It is because certain groups of individuals have the same heredity and thus the same fundamental traits that they rank as of one species. The practical test (not infallible, but generally applicable) of a valid species is that its members cannot interbreed with allied groups, which also rank as valid species. The process of evolution would be chaotic, instead of orderly, if individuals of widely different basic traits could interbreed, and produce fertile offspring.

On the other hand, there is a point of divergence , as concerns traits less fundamental, yet important, at which interbreeding is still possible, and may be highly advantageous. A so-called "outcross" is recognized among breeders of fancy domestic stocks as often beneficial. Among wild life, there is a constant tendency to inbreeding, which is not in itself disadvantageous, but which tends to produce specialized breeds, highly adapted for life in the given environment, but correspondingly unadapted for life elsewhere, or to meet changing conditions.

When an individual of the same species that has been reared in a widely different region comes into such a community, there is opportunity to test his specialized qualities, in comparison with those of the local residents, by the Mendelian process. And this, precisely, is what happens constantly in nature. It is such intermingling that furnishes the dominant *motif* in the plan of progressive evolution.

The so-called "mutations" that arise with seeming suddenness and give foundation for the development of new species are usually (in my opinion) due to the crossing of strains that are near the point of mutual infertility because of long residence in different regions. In no other way are radical departures from the old racial traditions likely to be initiated in a region where the environmental conditions are subject to little change. More than that—the tendency to variation thus induced will be advantageous in permitting a species to be modified to meet the new conditions of a changing environment. Lacking such stimulus, the species might be unable to change rapidly enough to escape extinction.

The point of application of all this is that little Eohippus—whom we may seem to have forgotten—and his contemporaries, placed amidst changing climatic (and therefore general) conditions, had developed precisely the traits of alertness and mobility that would lead them to change their habitat on occasion, covering relatively wide territories in quest of fresh pastures. Thus they not only encountered new conditions to which their organisms would respond, but came in contact with other tribes of their species from yet wider territories, with whose representatives they would exchange newly-acquired traits by interbreeding.

Long generations of such interbreeding lay back of the bigger toe of little Eohippus. That characteristic had been tested in the Mendelian crucible over and over, before its utility had been established. And when, as time went on, there were further tentatives, toward a still greater preponderance of the central toe and the corresponding neglect of the others, these variations would also be tested in the same way. And they would be accepted finally as distinctive traits of the species only if they proved an aid to the swifter running on which the life of the Eohippus tribe so largely depended.

In the end, it was to be made clear that the single toe had signal advantages. The side toes were subordinated in the millions of generations to follow, and a few of the descendants of little Eohippus would leave their remains as fossils in the rocks, even as he had done, for permanent record of the evolutionary changes by which the race was modified. Specialization in development of the central toe was coincident with ever-increasing size of body.

Had a complete series of individual skeletons, representing every minute modification, been preserved, it would be hard to say where the species Eohippus ends, and the species Proterohippus, of the later Eocene, begins. It would be equally hard to differentiate the latter from Mesohippus of the Oligocene and Prohippus of the

Miocene, with their successively nearer approximations to the ideal of a single toe, at which the even more recent Equus, or modern horse, arrives. That each in turn is the lineal descendant of the one before, there is no question. The case for Evolution, were the *fact* of evolution any longer in dispute (as it has not been, among well-informed people, these past fifty years), might be rested on the fossil records of the descendants of little Eohippus, representing a series of creatures unquestionably entitled to rank as valid and independent species.

The fact of the origin of species by evolution is not likely to be challenged by anyone who has examined attentively the family records of the little pro-horse of the Eocene.

XI

HEAD·ON

THE terrain across which little Eohippus scampered
—and in scampering developed the middle toe that
was his badge of distinction—was the same that had been
the habitat of the sluggish reptilian monsters of the pre·
ceding era. But it would hardly have been recognized
by its erstwhile inhabitants, could they have been aroused
from their long slumber. In the quarter·billion·year
period that had elapsed since the great reptiles were at
the climax of their reign, the land they inhabited had
been thrust northward to a distance of more than a
thousand miles. Favorite central regions that were then
within ten degrees of the equator had now passed be·
yond the confines of the tropic zone. The central part
of the old Dinosaur habitat was now well within the
north·temperate region, under climatic conditions that
the sun·loving reptiles could not have tolerated.

But for the warm·blooded, hair·covered mammals that
were now dominant, this was an ideal territory. Their
bodies protected by a coat that became heavier as needed;
their young in snug harbor during pre·natal infancy;
they could extend their habitat far toward the northern
border of the continent — now beyond the fiftieth
parallel. The herbivores of cursorial habit could retire
somewhat to the southward in the winter. Some other
members of the clan could and did learn to hibernate.
Yet others, mostly of carnivorous habit, preying on shell·
fish, fish, birds, and small quadrupeds as hardy as them·

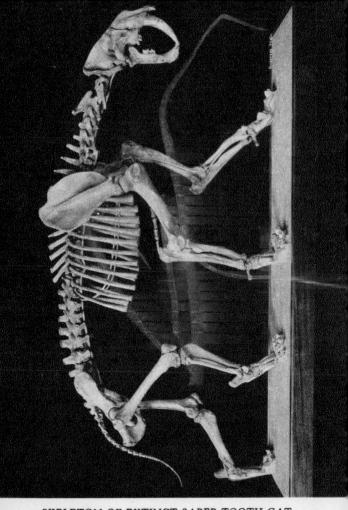

SKELETON OF EXTINCT SABER-TOOTH CAT

SABER-TOOTH CAT AND GROUND SLOTH

selves, developed coats of fur almost impervious to cold, and defied the utmost rigors of the climate.

The vegetation had become more and more "modern" in character. Hardwood trees and shrubs abounded; there were palms, along with reminiscent cycads and tree-ferns in the warmer latitudes; and the luxuriant grasses, gaining a foothold on soils long prepared for their coming, furnished Eohippus and his cursorial confrères with grazing facilities of a type previously unknown—tho the grasses had been introduced in the preceding era.

The physiographic conditions of the period, however, were by no means altogether reposeful. The cataclysm that had resulted in the vast Rocky Mountain upheaval, and the casting off of the Asiatic end of the continent, had aftermath in perennial volcanic and earthquake activities. There were vast outpourings of volcanic ash and tufa, repeated in the same region so persistently as to pile up rock formations thousands of feet in depth, sometimes incorporating vegetable and animal relics in profusion.

The east-and-west axis of the continent, centrally, was as usual elevated, constituting a watershed, with rivers flowing in either direction; but the main drainage was toward the south, with deposit of sediment that tended to weigh down the southerly border to the point of submergence. In particular the European segment of the double continent was largely submerged, as to its southern moiety, constituting a vast sea (the "Tethys" of Suess) with the not distant coast of Africa for its southern border.

Danger that this gap would be closed and the two continental masses brought into collision was for a long time apparent, especially as the eastward swing of the northern continents—balancing the westward swing of Asia—brought the European segment more and more directly in the path of the ever-advancing Africa. Actual contact appears to have been established before the Eocene period was over, perhaps more than once, with resultant upfoldings of strata in northern Africa and in the Eastern Alps region of Europe; and with general disturbance of the American terrain, registered as far west as the Rockies.

The elevation of the Pyrenees in the succeeding period (Oligocene) presumably resulted from another time of grazing contact, during which both continental masses were moving too closely in the same direction to produce more than minor catastrophes. The vast crumpling that is registered in the Swiss Alps and the series of upfoldings and overthrusts making the great east-and-west elevation as far as the Caucasus, at the extreme border of Europe, seem to tell of an ultimate head-on collision, toward the close of the Oligocene. But the differentiation between the diastrophism of this period and the somewhat later and even more stupendous telescoping of continental masses that was to attend the collision of Asia with Lemuria is not clearly established.

More nearly contemporary with the impact of Africa on the European segment of the double continent, however, was the head-on collision of South America with the lower extremity of North America. The resultant upheavals and crumplings formed the laterally trending distortions of the Central American mountains, and the mountains whose tops now form the débris of the West Indian and Caribbean archipelagos.

As the trend of Africa was easterly (owing to its far advance across the equatorial belt—its northern border perhaps fifteen degrees north of the equator), while the

HUNTING THE WOOLLY RHINOCEROS

trend of South America, because it had not reached the equator, was westerly, the two impacts acted jointly to shove the two portions of the northern continent, already in part separated, in opposite directions; slowing up the easterly trend of North America, and permitting the gap that was to become the Atlantic Ocean to widen.

The further effects on the northern continent were registered in an accentuation of the volcanic phenomena of the western interior, associated with renewed up-heaval of the Rocky Mountain strata, together with general elevation of the western region of the continent, to form the great plateau, many thousands of feet high, through which the Colorado River cut its way as the strata rose. Thus was formed the Grand Canyon of the Colorado, which remains to this day (notwithstand-ing the lowering of its original upper border by erosion) one of the most spectacular geological exhibitions in the world.

AMERICAN MASTODON AND FOX

XII

THE TWO GREAT HUNGERS

AS we scan the organic world even casually in imagination, and reflect on the unending series of miracles by which Evolution has made living things more complex and more beautiful generation by generation, until exquisite birds and graceful mammals replace fish and amphibian and reptile, while perfumed flowers glorify a landscape that once knew only club-moss and cycad, we cannot well escape the feeling that the mechanism which has wrought such wonders must be in itself very intricate and mysterious.

And yet it appears that if we were privileged to look into Evolution's bag of tricks, only two factors could be found there. Two simple, elementary factors—shall we call them Urges?—with which to operate, in transforming a protozoan into a man; a diatom into a rose. The thing seems incredible, yet it appears to be simply true. Granted these urges, which were invented away back in the Archeozoic time of beginnings, all the rest followed as a matter of course. All that was required of Evolution was to stay on the job constantly enough to see that neither of these urges was mislaid.

It cannot have been a difficult task, after affairs got under way. For the names of the two Urges are—Food-hunger and Sex-hunger. Lacking the first of these, the individual would promptly perish. Lacking the second, the race would vanish in a single generation.

But neither one of these urges was ever absent from

CHIMPANZEE

any normal being during the three billion years since they were invented. Habits as old as that are hard to break.

Here and there an aberrant individual lacked one urge or the other; but for every such abnormality, there were billions of individuals that had their lives dominated by the double urge. And out of the activities that resulted, came all the miracles. A strange paradox, but a mere biological truism. Is there anything more esthetic in Nature than the petal of a flower? It is only a signal set for some passing insect, with whose connivance the sex-urge must be satisfied—or the plant species that grows the flower will vanish.

Meantime the leaves of the plant, sucking in air from which carbon dioxid may be extracted in the chlorophyl laboratories, partly satisfy the food-urge in one way, while the roots of the plant reach out for nitrogen and oxygen and hydrogen, and a score of elements in solution to complete the transaction.

How the two urges are satisfied in the animal world needs no telling. Nor is much imagination required to make us understand how the urges operate to bring about the changes of racial type that we call evolutionary. Basically, the process is merely this: The animal that most avidly satisfies the food-urge will grow largest, and by beating off rivals will be able more generally to satisfy the sex-urge—and thus will transmit its traits to a maximum number of offspring. So these urges will be strengthened, and whatever physical or mental traits have contributed to their opportunity for functioning will become the heritage of an increasing proportion of the race.

And there, in a nutshell, you have the whole story of Evolution—the motivation back of the struggle for exist-

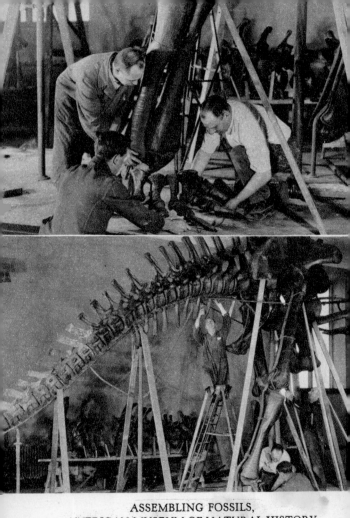

ASSEMBLING FOSSILS,
AMERICAN MUSEUM OF NATURAL HISTORY

ence; the mechanism of the survival of the fittest. It seems but a sordid basis for the development of brains that are organs of thought and the seat of esthetic sensibilities and poetic dreams and spiritual yearnings—but these things spring from that physical soil, as roses spring from the muckheap.

Let us follow the matter up a little, and note a few practical applications and consequences of the operation of the two urges. First of all, note that when any species has gained a reasonable foothold in any environment, it has potential power, were it unopposed, completely to overwhelm that environment. Take, for example, a fish which normally lays, say, a million eggs. Under favorable conditions, each egg becomes a fish; and since (by present hypothesis) they are unopposed, each female member of the company in turn lays a million eggs. The young fish that come from those eggs, to the number of 500,000,000 are the grandchildren of the original pair. Their grandchildren will have a census that you may compute by putting down 125 and adding eighteen ciphers—quintillions, that would be called, I suppose, if there were any reason for naming so preposterous a number.

Follow up the computation as far as you like. You will readily believe the estimate that computes a number of fish adequate to fill the oceans of the world in a very few more generations—packed in like sardines in a box. And if fish could live out of water, they would soon make a solid mass covering the world, and extending out as far as the moon—or as much farther as you care to follow their fortunes with a lead pencil.

Not all animals lay a million eggs, to be sure. But the principle of increase by geometrical ratio holds for all. There is no species of animal or bird that does not normally produce more than two offspring to the pair, in a lifetime. Ordinary species produce from ten to a thousand times that. And all that is required is *time* enough for even the least prolific of animals to duplicate the imagined feat of the fish that laid the million eggs. The tiniest of feathered creatures, the hummingbird, lays never more than two eggs to the clutch. But if every hummingbird lived the normal span of life, and nourishment could miraculously be supplied, hummingbirds would soon clog the air everywhere on the globe.

Apply the same principle to each and every living organism. You see at once what is meant by the term "Struggle for existence." It is sheer physical struggle, in the sense of competition for nourishment. And it will readily be seen that the keenest competition of all is likely to obtain between members of the same species. Most species have a restricted habitat; have become adapted to the condition of a particular zoological "zone," and, within that zone, occupy only particular areas—say of woodland, of prairie, of swamp, of arid field, or what not—and do not know how to make their way to advantage elsewhere. And that, of course, makes competition even keener.

Hence the advantage of mere physical bulk, and the tendency we see illustrated over and over for evolution to develop larger and larger animals—trilobites two feet long back in the Silurian; fish thirty or forty feet long in the Devonian; reptiles a hundred feet long in the Mesozoic. Brawn and more brawn. But note too the penalty. The ultimate premium, here as elsewhere, is not on the extreme, but on the happy mean. The overgrown creature beats off competition, and leaves maximum numbers of progeny that inherit its oversize. Then the environment changes. The continent is drifting into less sunny latitudes; the vegetation is no longer quite so luscious. There begins to be a threat of food-shortage.

Now the very quality that made the beast dominant— its size—begins to be a disadvantage. The food-urge is more and more difficult to satisfy. Presently it cannot be satisfied for the larger beasts. No matter now whether many offspring are produced; if born, they are born to starve. The race of giants dwindles. Some little, obscure member of the family perhaps survives—as frogs and salamanders are almost the sole survivors of the great amphibians of the Carboniferous; or as lizards and snakes survive the monsters of the Mesozoic.

Meantime, as we have repeatedly seen, some dwarfling tribe that has developed a new trait, under stress of adversity, competes so successfully—at first because of its very obscurity—that it presently overpopulates its habitat. Then begins over again the process of developing giants, for future elimination along the same route that their predecessors followed to oblivion.

After the disappearance of the great Dinosaurs and their allies, there was a relatively long period when there were no land-giants in the world. The small mammals whose day was dawning had opportunity to develop along many lines, without competition from alien tribes that could physically overwhelm them; but with ever-increasing competition from fellow-mammals. A partial solution of the food problem was found in the cultivation of specialized methods of securing food. Some creatures, for example, went into the trees, and remained there. Some stayed on the ground, and developed their legs, to enable them to graze and browse over wide territories. Some went into the sea, in emulation of the fishes. And as overcrowding tended constantly to bring about food-shortage, particularly since the tropical zones that make

SABER-TOOTH CAT AND CERVALCES (DEER-ELK)

for profuse vegetation were now left behind, an increasing number of creatures—ever pressed by the food-urge—were expanding their bills of fare: eating insects, the eggs of amphibians, snakes, and birds; and on occasion the young of other animals.

In other words, these creatures were becoming omnivorous; and were by way of becoming altogether carnivorous of habit. And for such creatures the advantages of increased size, strength, agility, and personal courage are obvious. Any slight variation of physique that made for such advantages was sure to be of such aid to its possessor that he could better satisfy the primal urges; and thus the advantage would soon come to be a racial heritage.

With few if any other organs does natural selection have better opportunity to show what it can do than with the teeth. These are the food organs *par excellence,* and good teeth are often a passport to longevity, while bad teeth are usually the equivalent of a death sentence, for creatures living under normal conditions of stress and over-competition.

Now teeth, representing a comparatively late experiment in animal architecture, tended to vary, and every variation was pretty sure to be either slightly advantageous or the reverse. If advantageous, it would be preserved by Mendelian inheritance; if disadvantageous, it would be weeded out. On occasion it might happen that a variation that seemed disadvantageous proved useful for a new purpose. An enlarged canine (eyetooth), for example, might seem less than useless for grazing, but might be very helpful in holding on to a frog that was endeavoring to escape being eaten. So enlarged canines would come into fashion with one particular family, and that family would have therein a distinct advantage.

Repeat the process for enough generations, taking advantage of the fact that variations in a certain direction seem rather inclined to repeat themselves—it never rains but it pours—and you have a race of creatures with canines extending far beyond their other teeth. Such teeth would be in the way for grazing—but by this time the owner of the teeth has ceased to graze. His other teeth have been modified, and would suit the purpose of grass-chewing not at all. But they do suit admirably the purpose of cutting up flesh, and are even suitable for crunching bones, to get marrow and mineral matter.

There have, of course, been other adaptive changes of the entire body of the animal, to match the changing teeth. The same process of trial and error, applied to here and there a seemingly chance variation (often superinduced, really, by the mingling of strains of creatures from widely separated habitats—the out-cross effect), has resulted in the development of a new type of animal architecture. In fact, several new types. One type has long, curved, retractile claws and a low-hung, gracile body, made for strength, and with legs built for best leverage in springing. This may be called the Feline type. It proved so effective a machine-form that all cats, whatever their size or wherever they might wander, were to retain it.

Another family developed a longer type of face, a rangier body, and legs with lengthened ankles, suitable for far-running. This was the wolf type, or dog type, and it also was to prove perennially popular. A third family developed a really incredible long-drawn-out body, almost eel-like in its tenuity—an exaggeration even of the type of the Mosasaur reptiles, now extinct. The legs became fin-like flippers — through endless generations of evolutionary trial and error—and the tail also fish-like in function, but broadened laterally instead of vertically. The earliest of these strangely modified mammals was called a Zeuglodon. It was to leave descendants a good deal less eccentric in form, but like it in habit—the whales.

Then there were other families that compromised between the land-form and the sea-form, and became in habit amphibious, tho very different in essential functions from authentic amphibians. These became sea-lions, seals, and walruses. And yet another family that retained land-locomotion equipment much more fully, yet learned to hunt chiefly in the water, became the progenitor of the races of otters and mink.

Thus the great tribe of Carnivores, with its strangely varied membership, was established in the early day of the Tertiary. And this, as we shall see, was but one of numberless miraculous transformations wrought by Evolution, through persistent application of her great basic principle of the two hungers, or urges, before the Age of Mammals reached its climax.

SHOVEL-TOOTH AND SIBERIAN MASTODONS

XIII

ELEPHANTS FROM AFRICA

IT must not be overlooked that masses of land of continental proportions exert a mutual gravitation-pull of significance when they lie close enough together to have the line between their centers of gravity differ widely from the direction of the earth's center. This pull no doubt operated to keep Lemuria, Africa, and South America in closer contiguity than they would otherwise have remained, during the period when all three were free, and moving northerly in the order of mention.

All three continents were of relatively low elevation, since none of them had been subjected to the mountain-making stresses that contorted the northern continent, so that their disturbance of the lateral equilibrium of their hemisphere was correspondingly slight, and possibly not sufficient to overcome their mutual gravitational pull. By the same token, the grip on them of inertia would be correspondingly feeble, so that their northward drift would be at low average speed. The speeding-up process incident to the glacial elevation of the Permian was of course not permanent—tho the momentum thus acquired would not immediately be counteracted by frictional resistance, and may perhaps have been instrumental in keeping the continents under way when they might otherwise have faltered.

On the other hand, the continents must have grown more rapidly as their larger areas entered the tropical zone, and such enhancement of mass would of course

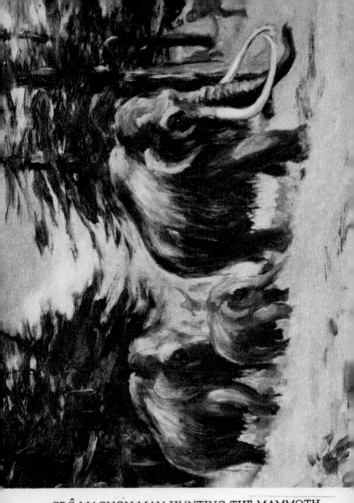

CRÔ·MAGNON MAN HUNTING THE MAMMOTH

act in the other direction. It would be mass added to the already overheavy southern hemisphere, and in proportion as the lack of balance between the two hemispheres (in part compensated by the appearance of Holarctica above the equator) was thus again accentuated, the northward movement of all the continental masses would be expedited.

The net result was that the dismembered portions of ancient Holarctica continued to move northerly. The American and European segments, however, because of the impulses imparted by their southern helpers, moved perhaps somewhat more expeditiously. In any event, the easterly end of Holarctica appears to have been at all times somewhat more northerly than the Asiatic end. This was an attempt, perhaps, to swing toward a great circle. The northern border of North America, which now slopes sharply to the southeast (there is a 20-degree difference between the two upper corners of the continent), then tipped in the other direction, in line with the northern border of Europe, which at present tips sharply southwesterly. The two territories were of course continuous throughout the long history of Holarctica, and the severance that now took place was to be but temporary. As the three isolated continents drifted poleward, they must, in the nature of the case, be brought nearer and nearer together at their northern borders, until contact was reestablished, if previously broken— as it perhaps never had been in case of America and Asia.

These rather tiresome geographical details are necessary, because the physical fact of continuity of territory between the three members of the former coalition, as existing throughout most of the long period of the Age of Mammals, must be clearly apprehended. There

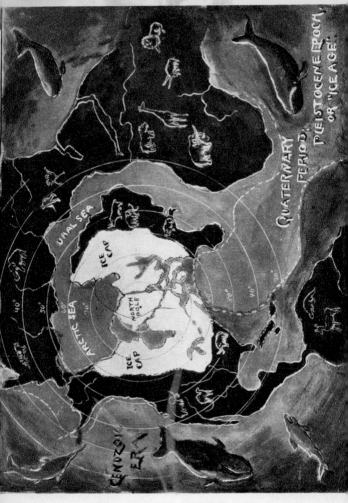

THE MOST RECENT ICE AGE

was full opportunity for exchange of populations, along routes that necessarily lay well within the warm temperate zone throughout most of the era—because only toward the close of the Tertiary period did any part of any continent pass into the Arctic zone. Even then, the land connection between America and Asia—the present Bering Strait region — was perhaps not farther north than the fortieth parallel, and the presence of the Pacific Ocean, shut off from Arctic currents, permitted climatic conditions at least as mild as those of present-day southern California.

Here, then, was a channel of communication between Asia and America, adequate for the mammalian population, tho it would hardly have sufficed for the reptilian hordes of the elder day. In the time of the great reptiles, however, as we know, the territory of Holarctica was unbroken, and the existence of Dinosaurs of closely similar type in Siberia and America requires no explanation. We should expect, however, to find greater diversity between the species of reptiles of eastern Russia and those of Siberia than between either and the reptiles of America—since the regions now contiguous on the two sides of the Ural mountain range were, according to present hypothesis, at that time opposite ends of a ten-thousand-mile continent.

In the later Tertiary time, however, as the continents drifted to the narrower-circled latitudes toward the pole, the "Ural Sea," which represents the gap that was 14,000 miles wide when Holarctica was at the equator, necessarily closed to a comparatively narrow channel, constituting, in the view of the earlier physiographers, a channel of connection between the great Mediterranean (Tethys) and the Arctic Ocean. In the present view, it was the remnant of an ocean—the universal

PREHISTORIC AMERICAN BISON

ocean that encompassed the northern hemisphere, which, by the encroachment of the now dismembered Holarctic continent had been separated into Pacific, Atlantic, and Arctic segments.

In any event, the Ural barrier existed, and while it lasted, there could be no trekking of land animals between Europe and Asia—except *via* America. The Ural Sea, at the time when the earlier interchanges of mammalian populations took place throughout Holarctica (as the three dissevered continents are still conveniently dubbed), was still of oceanic proportions—perhaps two thousand miles in width at the northern border in the late Eocene period, and not much less in the Miocene, the mid-period of the Age of Mammals.

Up to that time, then, the animals that spread from America to Europe, and those that made the journey in the opposite direction, must have traveled by a direct route, across the continuous territory of, say, New England and Old England—the latter being, of course, part of the unbroken terrain of western Europe. Even a good deal farther to the south, along the present seaboard of the central States, the connection may have held, against the encroachment of the forming Atlantic, well past the middle of the Tertiary period.

By this direct route, it would appear, the camels that originated in the land of Eohippus, there in southwestern America, went to Europe, and on to Africa. By the same route, the elephants that originated in northern Africa came to America. The earlier pachyderms, called mastodons, were not true elephants, tho closely allied, but the simon-pures came after, and flourished on our continent for millions of years. At a later day, some of them braved the inclemencies of a climate come to be frigid as the northerly drift continued, developing coats

STEGOSAUR, FOSSIL AND LIVING ARMADILLOS

of fur, and learning to subsist on the coarse foliage of conifers. But in the early period there was no call for such heroic expedients, which at best could but postpone the day of final departure. In the Miocene, the southern regions of America, Asia, and Europe alike lay well within the hospitable subtropical zone.

While such exchange of subtropical populations was taking place between Europe and America, there was similar exchange between the two Americas, along the highway that is now the abbreviated Isthmus of Panama, and the adjoining territory, now under water. From the south came strange mammals of primitive types, including even Marsupials (the opossum is the modern remnant), and Edentates, only one or two stages less primitive, such as the giant ground-sloths and massive armadillos.

A strange population, according to the modern view. But destined to thrive for millions of years, until the continent, forever retreating from the sun, carried its passengers into latitudes where, of necessity—since all life comes from the sun, and nothing grows without adequate light—the conditions of living were prohibitive. Then some creatures (as represented by their descendants) retired to South America, and the rest perished—except, of course, the small minority of relatively commonplace creatures (deer, wolves, bears, rodents) that evolved in such a direction that they became adapted to the transformed climatic conditions.

But that suggestion carries us far ahead of the story. Our concern of the moment is with creatures that had developed in a tropical climate, and existed under conditions not very different from those that had fostered the development of the giant populations of the Mesozoic. The great reptiles had vanished from Holarctica

EXTINCT ELK AND LIVING ELK AND MOOSE

partly because climatic conditions had become for them unendurable. But northern Africa was squarely in the tropic zone. No doubt the big reptiles lingered there much longer; but in the end they yielded to mammalian competition. As always, the bigger brains won.

The mammalian creatures that came nearest to duplicating the architectural plan, so to speak, of the great saurians were the elephants of which we were just speaking. We have learned of their coming to America. Perhaps something more should have been said of their early development, there in the tropical regions of Africa. The earliest ancestral mammals were developed in Holarctica, as we have seen. We have heard, also, of the strenuous competition that obtained there, as the various branches of the furry tribe expanded and flourished. Under such conditions, there is relatively rapid spread (emigration) of species, in every available direction.

Contact having been established between Europe and Africa (the present Alpine barriers by no means so formidable as they afterward became), multitudes of creatures emigrated southward—toward the sun. Among these was one family that was destined to develop bodies along altogether new lines, as regards in particular the head and face. By slow tentatives—with relative celerity, as viewed in retrospect — Evolution pushed ahead with an experiment in lengthening the jaws and modifying the teeth for digging. Then the lips were lengthened, to reach beyond the jaws. Finally the lower jaw was shortened, and the upper lip lengthened to grotesque proportions, including the nose with it—to form a new type of structure, called a "proboscis."

The creatures that were the subjects of this strange experiment were at the same time led to expand their bodies to what may quite literally be described as ele-

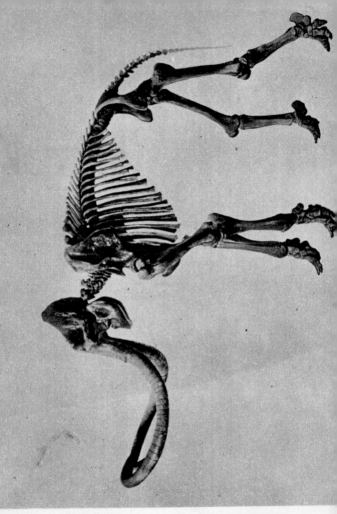

SKELETON OF AMERICAN ELEPHANT

IMPERIAL ELEPHANT IN CALIFORNIA (TAR PIT)

PRONGHORN ANTELOPE AND EXTINCT CAMELS

phantine proportions, since the final product is called an elephant. There were, naturally, long periods of intermediate development, during which the original fox-sized ancestor was being magnified, age by age, toward the vast bulk ultimately attained.

There were coincident changes in the teeth, if possible even more extraordinary. At one stage, all the front teeth except two outer incisors (in each jaw) were suppressed, and the incisors absurdly lengthened, becoming tusks. Later, the lower tusks were themselves abandoned, and the lower jaw further shortened, for convenience of the proboscis (or trunk), and the two upper tusks were extended, first slightly upcurved, in the mastodon, then ridiculously further upcurved, in the true elephant. The earlier species of elephants, which became extinct, are called mammoths. We shall see more of them in a later chapter.

In any popular appraisal, mastodons would pass for elephants, and nothing else. Technically, as viewed by the evolutionist, they are still one stage removed from true elephant standards—the difference being largely a matter of teeth. For many evolutionary stages the family motto had been "fewer and bigger teeth," and this applied not merely to the two incisors that remained to become monster tusks, but to the chewing teeth—the molars—as well. Ultimately only one double-pair of molars remained, permanently, each tooth of gargantuan size. The chewing surface, which had been deeply corrugated in the mastodon, was flattened and characteristically ridged with enamel in the perfected product that marks the true elephant—extinct mammoth and living representatives alike.

These great creatures, in size reminiscent of the Dinosaurs, could not well have developed except amidst luxu-

PREHISTORIC BISON AND IMPERIAL ELEPHANT

riant surroundings, as to vegetation; but they had intelligence enough to adapt themselves to alien conditions, as we shall see later. The story of their emigration to Holarctica has already been outlined. It remains here only to add that, toward the later stages of the Pliocene (the terminal period of the Tertiary), a direct route between Africa and the Americas may have been available, across the region that is now the West Indian Archipelago and the Caribbean Sea. Further reference to that possibility will be made in another connection. It is even possible that this was the main route, conceivably the only route, by which the true elephants (mammoths) came to America.

Be that as it may, they did come to America, and we shall meet them here in due course. It may be added that certain other overgrown mammals, like the ancestral manatees, or sea-cows, came with them, or at least from the same geographical region; and that the ancestral whales developed also from collateral branches of the pro-elephant stock, in the same general environment.

Only one mammal of comparable size, the walrus, was ever to be evolved in Holarctica. The development of that Brobdingnagian was made possible solely by aquatic habits and fish diet. Northern Holarctica had now become no place for the evolvement of bulky vegetarians.

PITHECANTHROPUS, EOANTHROPUS,
NEANDERTHAL MAN AND MODERN

XIV

THE RISE OF THE PRIMATES

ALL down the hundred-million-year stretch of time during which the descendants of little Eohippus, the primordial horse, were specializing more and more in the development of that (for their cursorial purpose) all-important *middle* toe, a certain group of their remote cousins had striven with equal assiduity, generation after generation, to develop the potentialities of the *first* toe.

What these potentialities were, even the most highly developed human intelligence of a later day could by no chance have divined. In the view of the champions of the middle toe, the first toe had no utility at all—and the second and fourth and fifth were no better. No other tribe of the mammalian clan would have gone quite so far as that, but all would have agreed that middle toes are better than outside toes. And it would have been conceded without much argument that if any toe were to be dispensed with, the first is the one that could best be spared.

That is to say, this would have been conceded by everybody except the members of the one nonconformist family, who were endeavoring to put the first toe of each foot to a new and rather absurd use. These iconoclasts—tho conservative enough as to the retention of five toes—seemed to feel that something might be gained if the first toe were enlarged instead of lessened in size, and adjusted somewhat out of line with the

EOANTHROPUS — THE "DAWN MAN"

ZULU WARRIOR

other toes, so that a certain grasping effect was possible.

But what good could there be in that? It made a decidedly deformed foot—not at all pretty to look at. And as for grasping, what better could you ask than the graceful clawed foot of, for instance, the squirrel? And whether for clasping or for any other purpose, you could not possibly compare the clumsy big-toe foot with the marvelous taloned paw of any member of the growing tribe of Felines, or blood-drinkers.

Of course no one was there to make such comparisons and criticisms as this, but had there been, their arguments would have seemed valid. Surely there could be nothing promising about the experiment of developing the one toe of the entire group that all other lines of experiment had found wanting.

But the triumphs of evolution are not attained by prophecy. They are attained by the method of trial and error. Mendelian selection furnishes the key, as we saw in considering the case of little Eohippus. Once the big-first-toe experiment had started, it was bound not to be given up till carried to a final issue in the practical field. If there were any advantage in being able to grasp things with a bigger first toe, Natural Selection, utilizing the Mendelian principle, would soon find it out.

And apparently there was an advantage. For as time went on, the wearers of bigger first toes did not decline in number, but increased. Moreover, the big toes became yet bigger; and in particular they became more and more opposable to the other toes—so that the foot as a whole was better and better adapted for grasping. Presently the opposition was so complete that you could put your big toe on one side of a limb and the other toes on the other side, and grip so tightly that you could swing your body free in the air. What other animal could safely do

NEANDERTHAL MAN; EARLY STONE AGE

CRUSHING SEEDS WITH STONE IMPLEMENT

CARIBOU AND (EXTINCT) MAMMOTH, ALASKA

PREHISTORIC KITCHEN MIDDENERS — MODERN
PATAGONIANS

that? Moreover, the opposing toe, especially on the fore foot, could be used in grasping small objects various and sundry—such as insects and tree-frogs, and other delectable articles of diet.

And now there was no longer any question about the utility of the enlarged and misplaced first toe. A toe that enabled one to climb better than before, and even to swing from tree to tree, while also aiding in the securing of food, was an instrument to be prized—and if possible bettered.

But what about that matter of betterment? It is clearly possible that the possessor of a fairly well-working opposable big toe may improve the efficiency of action of that organ by practise in its use. There can be no dispute as to that. But is this gain, or any part of it, transmissible to the offspring of that individual? Ah, that is quite another question. It is a question regarding which there has been radical difference of opinion in the biological world for fifty years or so (following the pronouncement, which then seemed heretical, of Weismann), but which the present biographer long ago answered, to his own satisfaction, in the affirmative.

This is no place for argument on this biological subtlety. On the other hand, the question has far too great significance, from the standpoint of evolution, to be ignored. Let it be said, then, with undogmatic brevity, that in the present view each individual animal organism is a unity, every cell of which is dependent on every other cell. No change of structure or of function can be made that does not influence the remotest cell—including the cells that make up the *genes*, or heredity factors, in the chromatin of the germ plasm. So every improvement of the individual will be passed on (with the Mendelian qualification) to the offspring of that organism.

EARLY USE OF FIRE

But this statement requires instant interpretation. The *amount* of gain that any offspring can thus secure is to be measured in comparison with the aggregate gains along similar lines of all the past generations. This means that the modification that can be wrought in a single generation is infinitesimal in the proportion of one to many millions. The most fatuous experiment ever recorded in the annals of biology was Weismann's experiment of cutting off the tails of ten successive generations of mice, and measuring to find whether the tenth generation had inherited shorter tails. Of course he found no measurable difference. Yet, according to the present view, the difference was there. Only, it was a difference to be measured in billionths of an inch—representing the power of ten generations of tailless mice, against the power of the billion generations of tailed mice that preceded them since vertebrate history began.

Understand, then, that the change wrought in a single generation through the transmission of what is termed an "acquired" character (unless by direct traumatism of the germ plasm) is infinitesimal. Admit that the heritable effect of functional practise is of necessity immeasurably small. But—reflect that Evolution deals with numberless generations, and we realize that the cumulative effect of effort in a given direction may in the end be not merely measurable, but transformative. Granted time enough—generations enough—the perpetual use of the bigger toe, and the perennial striving for its better use, result in the final evolution of an opposing toe that we may call a "thumb," attached to a member called a "hand."

Meantime the impressions gained by the grasping member with its developing thumb and fingers will

TWO VIEWS OF STONEHENGE, ENGLAND

RUINS OF LAKE-DWELLER VILLAGE
—
ALINEMENT OF MENHIRS IN BRITTANY

LATER STONE AGE

perennially have been transmitted to a central nervous system that becomes a more and more intricately developed brain—a storehouse of energy; a clearing-house for impressions that in association become concepts; an inhibitor and re-director of responses—in a word, an organ of mind.

Such was in fact the outcome of the experiment with the bigger first toe, which the distant cousin of little Eohippus inaugurated, in defiance of precedent, back there in the early day of the Age of Mammals. And in the sequel, here toward the close of that period, we find whole races—a multitude of species—of evolved descendants of that early iconoclast, each with hands of extraordinary utility, and with brains so highly developed, in comparison with the brains of other creatures, as to make them incomparably intelligent animals, justifying the name *Primates*—the primary, or leading, members of the animal kingdom.

There are, of course, gradations of intelligence, as of form, among the members of this select company. In common with other tribes — Carnivores, Rodents, Horses, Elephants—they have wandered across the continents, and made themselves at home in all tropical and subtropical zones. Some of them—notably the monkeys of South America—have learned to make use of tails as prehensile organs, supplementing the use of hands and feet. Some retain tails, but make no such practical use of them—for example, Old World monkeys. Some have reduced their tails to mere apologies—as the apes. And a few, which chance to be the ones that have attained greatest size of body and brain (or was it chance?), have abandoned tails altogether, and are by way of giving up the arboreal habit of life.

These are the forebears of the Anthropoid apes—

A STONE-AGE BOWMAN

MODERN BOWMAN, TIERRA DEL FUEGO

CLIFF DWELLINGS, MESA VERDE PARK, COLO.

chimpanzee, orang, gorilla. And one other. That other —own cousin to the ones named, yet not precisely like any one of them, any more than they are precisely like one another—that other is the direct ancestor of a yet more highly developed Anthropoid whose appearance was even now imminent; one that would pass through stages of evolution in the ensuing millennia that would bring him to a dominant position, and cause the next epoch of the history of Mother Earth to be designated, in his honor, the Age of Man.

A SKYSCRAPER IN CAPPADOCIA

THE QUATERNARY PERIOD

(Anno Vitæ, 3,150,000,001—3,200,000,000)

The Quaternary Period of the Cenozoic Era opens
with the Pleistocene Epoch, or Ice Age, and concludes
with the Recent Epoch, or "Age of Man," which
merges into the historic present. There is no sharp
chronological line of demarcation between the two
epochs. The allotment of only fifty million years for the
entire period may seem an under-estimate, but it is
conditioned on the lack of evidence for the development
of any radically new evolutionary types in the post-
Tertiary period, and on the assumption that the reverse swing and lateral drift of the continents have been
exceptionally rapid, for reasons that will appear as the
narrative proceeds.

A STONE-AGE FAMILY

XV

THE GREAT BRAIN-MAKING
EXPERIMENT

GEOLOGISTS have much to say about the "Great
Glaciation," the "Colossal Ice-Sheet," the time of
refrigeration when, as it seemed from our viewpoint of
the moment, all the world was wrapped in the grip of
Arctic winter, and death and desolation were the sole
order of the day.

But Mother Earth, had she time to listen to these
doleful maunderings, must have smiled amusedly—if
not derisively—at these evidences of the strabismic
squint of her biographer. "A vast Glacial Epoch?" she
might have queried. "Where, then, was this great spec-
tacle staged? What *proportion* of our land surface did
it occupy? What *percentage* of plant and animal life
did it affect? Where, dear biographer, is your sense of
historical perspective, that you can indulge such fan-
tasies?"

And instantly the biographer stands corrected. He
can only plead in extenuation that the nearness of the
Ice Age made it loom for the moment quite out of its
true proportions—somewhat as a copper cent held near
the eye hides the sun. But thus corrected he is led to
reflect that the "vast" ice-cap was in reality confined to
segments of two minor continents. Its area, all told, was
perhaps half the size of the single continent of Africa;
much less than half the size of Asia.

And even that is accepting the glacier at its very

ANDAMAN ISLANDERS — AUSTRALIANS
WITH BOOMERANGS

PRIMITIVE MAT WEAVING

PRIMITIVE WEAVING — BASKETS AND CLOTH

MODERN WEAVING

best—when it attained its utmost limits, which were
held but for a relatively brief time. The main bulk of
the ice-cap was transient, doomed to disappear as the
continents began their return journey. It fought a hopeless battle against the sun at every stage. A losing fight,
of course, tho with intermittent periods of success as
the continental surface oscillated—sinking under weight
of the ice, and thus producing warmer conditions that
melted the ice itself; then rising again as the weight
lessened, and thus fostering renewed refrigeration. The
interglacial periods thus determined cut in largely on
the term of occupancy of the land by the glacier while
forecasting the inevitable outcome.

Even if the interglacial periods were ignored, however, and the reign of the glacier counted from its in-
ception to the final disappearance (up to the present)
of the ice-blanket, the time involved was almost negligible, in comparison with the vast eras of Mother
Earth's earlier history. It will be recalled that, according to the chronological scale adopted in our biography,
the Archeozoic era compassed 900 million years; the
Proterozoic, 600 million; the Paleozoic, 900 million;
the Mesozoic, 450 million — a total of 2,850,000,000
years. Round numbers, of course, but impressive, as
suggesting how long and strenuous had been the struggle of organic beings from the protozoan up merely to
the status of the small-brained king of the Dinosaurs—
for of course the Mesozoic terminated (by definition)
with the dropping of the curtain on the Age of Reptiles.

Mammals were on the scene at that time, to be sure.
But as yet they had reached only the stage of secure
promise. Their time of greatness was in the future—
and for that future, with all its potentialities to be made
realities, only a bare 350 million years remained.

Only 350,000,000 years for the task of Evolution, in remodeling and transforming types as yet partly reptilian into dominant mammals like whales, monstrous in size beyond the sharks; and colossal elephants, almost rivaling the Dinosaurs in bulk and vastly surpassing them in intelligence; and lions with the ferocity if not quite the size of the vanished Tyrannosaur; and horses with one big central toe and amazing ankles to give them undreamed-of speed; and monkeys with extraordinary opposable thumbs, and brains that—but again we are anticipating the story.

What I started to say was that only 350 million years remained for the Cenozoic era, which includes the Age of Mammals and the Age of Man—as against the 450 million that had been given over to the reptiles, not to mention the still earlier and even longer eras. And the crux of the matter was meant to be that when the Tertiary period or true Age of Mammals closed, 300 million years had been consumed, and only fifty million remained in which to accomplish the concluding miracle (as it must seem from the prejudiced human standpoint) of the creation by evolution of the relatively colossal brain and the really notable concomitant intelligence of Man.

A bare fifty million years in which to build up cell by cell the relatively small, smooth brain of a man-ape into the great nerve-cell storehouse (with surface deeply convoluted in order that myriads of thought-reservoirs may be housed in compact space) which is the brain of *Homo Sapiens;* the organ of thought of an Anaxagoras, a Plato, a Shakespeare, a Darwin. The time is too short; the task is impossible.

Yet that impossible task was to be accomplished—and therein lies the miracle. It was as if Evolution, the

PRIMITIVE COSTUMES, WITH DECORATIONS

YET MORE DECORATIVE

DWELLING OF AFRICAN PIGMIES

AFRICAN CHILDREN SPINNING COTTON

miracle-worker, in the long eras of striving, had learned to concentrate her efforts, to speed up the processes of transformation, to advance more surely, with fewer false steps, entering fewer culs de sac, envisaging the goal with surer vision.

Turning from metaphor to sober interpretation, we must concede that the miracle was not quite so great as at first glance it seemed. After all, there was no cataclysmic transformation to be effected. The true miracle had been accomplished ages before, when the early groups of nerve cells began to be evolved, and aggregated into convenient clusters, to form the first organic storage battery that could be called a nascent brain. Hundreds of millions of years had elapsed since then. The nascent brain had become a highly developed organ, its every essential part formed and adjusted where it could function to best advantage—as proved by the fact that no essential change would ever be found necessary or advantageous.

The brain of the pro-ape, there toward the close of the Miocene, differed from the brain of a Darwin only somewhat as the storage battery of a pocket flash-light differs from the storage battery that drives a truck. The brain of the primitive anthropoid was a storage reservoir for impressions; a central station for the coordinating of messages; an inhibiting station that controlled responses—in a word, an organ of thought. It adumbrated the human brain of the future precisely as the little electric top of Faraday, of one-mouse power, adumbrated the modern dynamo that propels a freight train. What was called for, in one case as in the other, was betterment of an invention already in operation.

Following up the chance illustration, note that it took thousands of years of experimentation on the part of

CANOES — ANDAMANESE AND AUSTRALIAN

OLD PLOWING (EGYPT) AND NEW

civilized man to produce the little pre-dynamo of
Faraday; and that the evolvement of the mechanism
from that toy-stage to the ten-thousand-horsepower
stage required but the brief span of a half-century.

In revised view, then, it no longer seems impossible
that worth-while things may be done with that uncon-
voluted brain of the man-ape in the short space of fifty
million years ahead. Yet there was no time to waste—
and you may be sure that Evolution wasted none. During those early days of the new period, the Pleistocene,
when the glacial display that distracted our attention
was being staged up there in the Arctic region—where
nothing worth while has ever happened or ever can
happen, there were multitudes of anthropoids down in
the tropics—where things do at least begin to happen—
that were experimenting eagerly in the particular task
of which we are speaking: the improvement of brains.

Not working with blue-prints, you understand. Not
guided by any foreknowledge of the mechanism of
brains. Not even aware that they had brains, or that
such a thing as an organ of mind existed. But working
effectively none the less—some individuals more effectively than others, of course; but every last anthropoid
working with assiduity, early and late, with entire disregard of any rules of the labor union. And in the end,
their joint efforts accomplished wonders—tho to be
sure, nothing much was accomplished in any one generation. These inventors were working for posterity.

What, specifically, did they do? Simply answered.
Each and every ancestral anthropoid seemed bent on
demonstrating that in the organic world there is no
embargo on perpetual motion. Perpetual activity was
their motto. They raced up and down trees, swung
helter-skelter from limb to limb, chased one another

PREHISTORIC WHEELS IN MODERN TURKEY

out onto slender branches where their lives were saved by a hair's breadth, and clambered to dizzy heights in quest of fruit, or just for the fun of climbing.

These activities called for use of all four feet—with their opposable first toes—in every conceivable attitude. But there were countless other activities in which the fore-feet were particularly requisitioned. The fore-feet, indeed, had now developed into what may as well be called "hands," once for all—instruments no longer confined to cursorial uses, but amazingly useful for grasping food, testing the qualities of anything that interested you, washing your face, scratching your nose, or even so delicate an operation as the removal of minute uninvited parasites from the furry head of your offspring.

What has all this to do with brains? Everything. No one of these movements, not even the very simplest, could be performed without the cooperation of the brain. No movement is made that is not directed from the brain, and signaled along nerve channels to the responsive muscles that do the physical part. And, contrariwise, there is no muscular action that is not telegraphed back to the brain, along another set of nerves, and registered there, as if by an automatic time-clock. Never does a finger of one of those flexible hands touch any object, to get its "feel" or test any of its qualities, but the impression is transmitted, and registered in the brain as a "sensation"—of heat or cold, of softness or hardness, of pleasant import or of unpleasant.

And every sensation thus registered in the brain is a permanent endowment. Every impression is stamped there, as truly as if each receiving cell were the photographic film of a movie camera. The brain that has received many impressions—the old brain—is as differ-

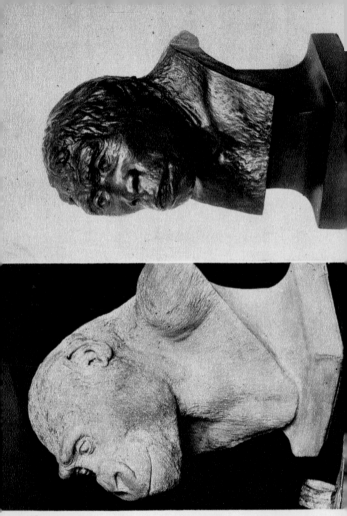

GORILLA AND PITHECANTHROPUS, THE APE-MAN

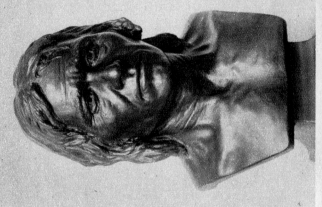

CRÔ-MAGNON MAN AND LIVING PATAGONIAN

PRIMITIVE AND LESS PRIMITIVE DWELLINGS

ent from the brain that has received few impressions—
the young brain—as the unexposed roll of cinema films
is from the same roll after the scene has been "shot."

And the mind which is, so to say, the obverse side of
the brain cells is no less changed. The storehouse of
registered impressions and resultant sensation—developed films—can be drawn on at will, counting as
"memory." And different departments of the storage
warehouse for sensations can be put into communication with one another, along telephone wires that everywhere connect the cells. Comparisons can thus be made
that form the basis for conclusions, or "ideas," about
the nature of the things various and sundry with which
the hands have come in contact.

There is similar coordination with other storage cells
that hold impressions gained through the organs of
special sense—eyes, ears, nostrils, palate. And such co-
ordinations prove exceedingly useful. One learns, for
example, to recognize a certain red fruit as delectable,
but learns also that it is undesirable to clutch at peculiar
types of thin-waisted insects. And so on through the
day's activities. Old experiments repeated; new ones
made. The brain storehouse getting crowded, and new
cells called for. New cells added in due course to meet
the need. Greater and greater complexity of memory
pictures, correlations, and attendant ideas.

In a word, progress in brain-building. And of course,
concomitant progress toward a bigger skull-case to hold
the brain; and more flexible fingers to gain better impressions; and a better muscular apparatus to carry out
more ambitious feats of agility; and a stronger bony
framework to hold the muscles; and new sets of teeth
better adapted to the more varied dietary adopted after
more intelligent experimentation. One want supplied,

PRIMITIVE SAILBOATS OF CEYLON

LESS PRIMITIVE SAILBOAT

another springs, as the old copy-book saw phrased it (tho with no intended reference to monkeys that were developing human brains, of course, lest one run afoul of the anti-evolution censor).

So, generation after generation, the good work went on, down, say, in Ethiopia, in a tropical land of plenty —at the very time when billions of creatures were dying of starvation up there in the north, in the unknown corner of the earth where the ice-sheet held sway. The death of the starvelings did not matter. But the increasing success of the brain-developing experiment was one of the most momentous trends in world-history. Incidentally, there were other billions of creatures in the tropics dying quite as meaninglessly as their contemporaries of the north—and dying mostly by claw and fang, which is no very notable gain on starvation.

For the matter of that, if you wish to press the point, there were only a few, even of the anthropoids, whose lives were other than meaningless, as regards effect on the great brain-making experiment. Only those that had progressed farthest, and by the best blend of qualities, established themselves in direct line of lineage of the finished product of the future. It was necessary that there should be a vast number of the experimenters, so that Mendelian tests of new traits might be made on a large scale—as the plant experimenter sows acres to seeds in order to select one choicest seedling. But in the sequel, only four pairs of parents in each generation would be responsible for the ideal couples of the next generation. Fortunately for pre-human pride, no one could know whether or not he was destined to hold a place in this select company.

As a matter of course, the general average of brains and bodies increased generation by generation. The super-anthropoid of any generation did not rise so very far above the rank and file of his contemporaries. The average anthropoid of any generation would rank far above the standard of, say, a hundred thousand generations before. But it remains to be said that such evolutionary advances could not continue indefinitely, unless the experimenters gave themselves opportunity to collate new experiences by changing their environment. Where they were now living, the environment itself would not rapidly change.

And that brings us to what is perhaps the most interesting part of the whole story. Some of the experimenters did change their environment—and thereby determined the continued success of the experiment. We are not to suppose, however, that any venturesome individual in particular decided one fine May morning to set out pioneering. That is not the way emigrations of animal populations come about. What happens is that a colony thrives and increases so abundantly that young couples setting up for themselves are obliged—by emphatic invitation of their elders—to go beyond the borders of the old colony and seek a new place in the sun.

A colony that thus spreads by quarter-mile stages has in the course of, say, a hundred thousand generations, traveled far; even tho the emigration has often been subject to interruptions, to reversals that momentarily set its boundaries back. Starting in Ethiopia, the colonists, vastly transformed, may find themselves in India. They have left partly transformed collateral branches all along the way. Other branches have emigrated concentrically in all available directions, some of them penetrating far to the south of Africa, others far to the north, into central Asia.

Changing conditions of environment have speeded

PRIMITIVE AND LESS PRIMITIVE
PASSENGER BOATS

up evolution, as always. Responsive change of the organisms was imperative. Racial extinction would be the penalty of conservatism. Numberless potential new races were thus cut off. But numerous others made good, and, by living, proved their right to live. All developed brains and bodies almost unrecognizably advanced from the old standards of the proanthropoid, back in the fatherland. But one line of descent, in particular, had, as it were, specialized in brain development. That, of course, is the line we have been following in imagination.

The members of this company, generation after generation, became more venturesome. They came finally to regions where the trees no longer grew to such size and in such profusion as to afford satisfactory permanent dwellings and feeding-places. If their colonies spread farther, the tree life must be to some extent abandoned. More and more, as generations passed, the experiment of progressing on the ground was tested. Gradually the leg bones were lengthened; the feet were adjusted to maintain weight on the ground, rather than for clutching the trunks and branches of trees.

There followed experiments in taking up a broken branch for support in walking; and this led to the discovery that such a stick could serve as a weapon of defense against aggressive co-residents. So now the transformed descendant of the original anthropoid could cope with creatures that would have toyed with his ancestor as a cat toys with a mouse. He could walk on two feet, partly erect, like the best of the ancient Dinosaurs. But his range of intelligence so far transcended that of any Dinosaur that—tho its basic elements were the same—it might seem to denote a mind of a new order.

And in particular, he used his hands to manipulate sticks and stones that served as weapons—and therein lay the greatest single advance in the history of organic life, as regards the practicalities of every-day existence. The ape that walked on two feet had become a user of tools. Now he held the future in the hollow of his hand.

Here the story need not be carried farther, except in barest epitome. It was inevitable that the big-brained user of tools should become bigger-brained, more erect, better and better able to use his hands for varied purposes. Before the new era was half over—while the Ice Age was still on, there at the north—his race attained the status of what was to be called in after time the erect ape-man (*Pithecanthropus erectus*) of Java. He had far outstripped his cousins, fine representatives in their way of collateral lines, known as Gorillas, Chimpanzees, and Orangs.

A few score thousand generations later, brain and body still farther developed along the same lines, he was a tool-maker as well as user, a domesticater of animals, a user of fire, a wearer of clothes. Each new accomplishment had been acquired only after long generations of tentative experimentation. And each had had a revolutionary influence on his manner of life—and in turn had led on to yet other advances. Wandering now into western Europe, while reminiscences of the Ice Age were still manifest, he left mementoes of his existence, and in particular physical relics, that would lead his remote descendants to dub him the man of Neanderthal (*Homo neanderthalensis*).

His race vanished, but collateral branches, not long severed from his branch of the family, came after him (perhaps accomplishing his destruction, in characteristic human fashion), and established themselves in the same

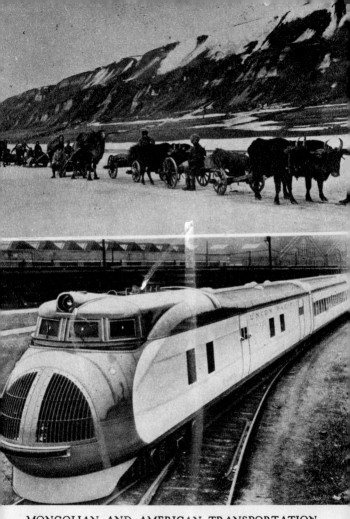

MONGOLIAN AND AMERICAN TRANSPORTATION

terrain, at a time when woolly elephant and rhinoceros and reindeer were his co-residents in western Europe. The mementoes of this new race were not only physical relics, but works of art—engravings on ivory, statues of clay, wall-paintings in color—which attest abundantly his title to rank as of the same species with his modern descendant.

This race has been called Crô-Magnon. It is merely a geographical appellation, but the Crô-Magnon stands level with his descendant of our day, with the proud specific title, *Homo sapiens*—modern Man, most sapient of Primates.

Long before this, you may be sure, he had acquired all the essential traits that mark the species. In seeking food, or in defense of his own, or in meeting the opposition of his fellows, he was the most vindictive and ferocious of killers the world had known. In the manner of attaining his ends he was crafty beyond any creature that had lived. In inventive ingenuity, he far surpassed even the man of Neanderthal, his predecessor. He elaborated vocal sounds into intricate texture of languages. He devised pictorial records that in time would evolve into hieroglyphics and then into alphabets. He dreamed dreams, and the brain that generated the dreams generated also the power to make the dreams come true. He became—as no animal before him had been—in some measure a shaper of his environment, and therefore in corresponding measure the arbiter of his own destinies.